You Don't Know
What It's Like

You **don't know** what it's like

Finding ways of building relationships with people with severe learning disabilities, autistic spectrum disorder and other impairments

Phoebe Caldwell

with

Dr Matt Hoghton

Pavilion

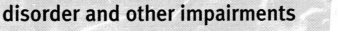

You Don't Know What It's Like

Finding ways of building relationships with people with severe learning disabilities who also have autistic spectrum disorder or other impairments that present us with 'difficult' behaviour

Phoebe Caldwell

with Dr Matt Hoghton MRCGP

Published by:

Pavilion Publishing (Brighton) Limited
The Ironworks
Cheapside
Brighton
East Sussex BN1 4GD

Telephone: 01273 623222

Fax: 01273 625526

Email: info@pavpub.com

Web: www.pavpub.com

First published 2000. Reprinted 2001, 2002, 2004.

ISBN 1 84196 023 3

Pavilion Publishing is committed to providing high quality, good value, current training materials and conferences, and bringing new ideas to all those involved in health and social care. Founded by health and social care professionals, Pavilion has maintained its strong links with key agencies in the field, giving us a unique opportunity to help people develop the skills they need through our publications, conferences and training.

Editor: Anna McGrail

Cover design: Bob Laker

Page design and typesetting: Stanford Douglas

Printed by: Paterson Printing Ltd

CONTENTS

Section 1

INTRODUCTION

For the past 25 years, at first working in large institutions and more recently as a travelling teacher in community settings, I have been looking for ways to develop relationships with people who are difficult to reach. Such people may have severe learning disabilities and are often very withdrawn, or have behaviour patterns which separate us from them. In either case, there is a gulf between us – a gulf of confusion, or perhaps anger and fear – that leads them to reject us and may lead us to reject them. The relationship between us becomes distorted – mothering or control may replace respect and solidarity. We do not know how to bridge the gap.

This book is a companion volume to *Person to Person*, which was the outcome of freelance work following four years of work supported by the Joseph Rowntree Foundation.[1]* It explores innovative ways of getting in touch with people who are difficult to reach. While its focus is on individuals with autistic spectrum disorder (ASD), it also includes reflections on other behaviours that we label as 'challenging' or 'maladaptive' behaviour. Not everyone with ASD has learning disabilities and, where an able person has severe ASD, this can mask their ability – they present as much less able than they are. However, there are people with learning disabilities who also fall within the autistic spectrum; it is this group that I shall mainly focus on in this book.

The book takes up the theme that each individual perceives the world differently but that this may be especially true of people with severe learning impairments whose behaviour we find difficult to work with. It does not set out to be an exhaustive manual. Rather, it is a series of reflections on the ways we think about and work with people with a wide range of disturbed behaviours. In all cases, it tries to look for creative ways of working which are based on understanding **what a person is experiencing** and **what it is that their behaviour is trying to tell us**.

---

*All references are individually numbered and given in full on page 113.

One of the book's starting points is a series of questions I was asked during a training day for managers of community homes for people with severe learning disabilities. The first questioner asked what I would do about a person who greeted the speaker every morning with personally offensive names. Would I agree that one should ignore undesirable social behaviour? The second said that, living as we do in a world where we are liable for our actions, should we not be thinking in terms of training the people we work with to take responsibility? The final questioner asked if I believed in punishment (as in punishment and reward). In the course of this book, I hope to address the attitudes that underlie these questions.

The other starting point is an incident that happened more than 20 years ago. I had just begun working with people with severe learning difficulties and challenging behaviour in a long-stay hospital which has since closed. A woman with very severe ASD was extremely upset. A colleague suggested she sit down. She put her face close to his and shouted:

> 'You don't know what it's like! You don't know what it's like!'

She was unable to elaborate on this cry for help – it was the only time we ever heard her speak – but I can hear her now. What she said has remained deeply engraved in my mind and periodically I have reflected on it.

Two different realities

At one end of the spectrum we meet the language of control and at the other, a cry for help, a window opening on a landscape of desperation. These two different realities stand in stark contrast to each other. On the one hand, we have our need to contain a variety of behaviours which may be unacceptable for one reason or another. On the other hand, we have an individual's cry for help which, in spite of goodwill, is not always being heard within the services we offer to people with learning difficulties/disabilities and disturbed behaviour.

Contemplating this divide, a colleague said:

> 'We need a new paradigm for working with challenging behaviour. We need to see it in a different way.'

Reviewing recent work on the 'theory of mind', Dunbar reminds us that although we are born egocentric, by the age of four we are able to understand that others may think and feel differently to ourselves.[2]

The problem is that, in spite of this intensionality – our capacity to know that another person can have a different point of view from our own – we do not always act on it. When I am teaching, I find that one of the things people find most difficult is to take into account that others may perceive the world we all share in a completely different way. In our day-to-day interactions we make enormous assumptions, based on our own sensory intake, about the way others are perceiving and processing their experience. This mind-set can also get built into strategies for care which, although well-meaning, do not allow for the ways in which a particular person encounters their world.

For example, a person with severe learning disabilities who also has ASD may find it extremely stressful to handle change – they do not have the flexibility to cope when an event turns out to be different to that which they had anticipated. They cannot marry the two different images, what they *expected* to happen with what is *actually* happening now. Nevertheless, we frequently persist in programming in opportunities for change on the grounds the person will 'get used to it'. However, this throws the person into an impasse and can be a trigger for rising stress and consequent 'difficult' behaviour. The situation can be stabilised by reducing the incidence of change and, if the change is predictable, working out ways of letting an individual know that it is going to happen so that they have time to work through the idea.

The purpose of this book is to help us set aside our own reality and enter into worlds which people are struggling to interpret, worlds where people respond to completely different sets of sensory perception to those which we experience in our so-called 'normal' world.

Subjective language and experience

An enquiry of this nature immediately runs up against the difficulties of how we can transfer our perceptions of feelings to each other, since the only language we have to describe them accurately is subjective.

As adults, we view the behaviour of other people through distant eyes – we see it from the outside, forgetting that it is also part of the range, or at least within the potential range, of our own responses. For example, those of us who experienced temper tantrums as children will recall the all-embracing explosion that can be triggered by conflict with reality. Nothing exists but over-the-top blind rage. Our response to frustration is as if we were life-threatened – and indeed the ego does feel itself to be in danger of extinction. We are swamped with adrenaline, we have 'become' our feeling. We are not accessible to reason.

It is interesting to put this insider's view of a temper tantrum alongside Bennett's analysis of the 'fight response'.[3] She describes the physical effects of adrenaline which accompany this and charts the build-up to aggression. In particular, she discusses the impact this has on crucial areas of functioning: the effects of adrenaline interfere with the ability to communicate, respond appropriately and think rationally, amongst other impairments. Bennett shows how we can identify the various stages of build-up through our observations of physical behaviour and discusses appropriate techniques to aid de-escalation.

Why then, if we can chart the progress of a difficult behaviour so accurately, should it also help us to know how it feels to experience it? For example, isn't it enough to 'know about' autism? Why should we need to know about what it *feels* like?

Part of the problem is that the word 'feeling' has different meanings. For some people, it is such an emotive word that they reject insight and empathy as ways of perception. Throughout this book, I use 'feeling' in the sense of how we experience sensory intake. I find it helpful to know how the person I am working with sees, hears, touches and is touched by the world, and if they perceive it differently from the way I do. I need to know this in order to avoid basing remedial and therapeutic strategies on the false premise that we are both operating from the same sensory model.

In this book, I want us to try to look at difficult behaviours from the inside – to walk into subjective experience deliberately, with our eyes wide open. We can then begin to view problems not just from a distance but to know what the people we are working with are feeling.

I am suggesting that, although this can be a dangerous path since it embraces the risks of projection, if we are not prepared to empathise in its deepest sense, we risk the equally hazardous alternative of omnipotence and control. To share feeling, even the attempt to share it, enlarges and deepens our understanding. At the same time, however, we have to monitor our perception, trying always to bring together the rational and the empathetic approaches. If we achieve this, we may uncover questions to be answered which we would have missed if we had maintained a detached standpoint.

Enhancing empathy

Because attempts to share the subjective experience of others can lead us into situations that are fraught with painful relationships, and also because to change a person's gender in the pursuit of disguise might render interactions psychologically untrue, I have used a variety of ways of presenting personal material. Wherever possible, permission has been sought. Where it has seemed that it might be damaging to raise the issue of permission, and where there are groupings of behaviours, I have made use of imaginative reconstructions, sometimes to the extent of complete personalisation, standing in for an individual, putting myself in their place. However, I must emphasise that all the encounters relayed in this book are factual, and actually happened.

While being aware of the dangers of projection, (grafting my feelings onto other people) and introjection (taking on board the feelings of other people and failing to distinguish between these and those which properly belong to myself), this approach has the advantage of enhancing empathy. Using material which is generally available (particularly that written by high-functioning people with ASD about their experiences of the world they live in), and ideas gained from talking to people who have some insight into their condition, together with fragments from my own work with individuals, I hope to be able to build up pictures that allow us to see how the world might be for others. I shall approach this task by asking such questions as:

- What messages is an individual getting from the world in which they live?

- Which of these messages has meaning for them?

- Which of these messages do they perceive as frightening, and is this is leading them to behave as they do?

- Can we meet their needs? If not, can we modify their environment?

Summary

In this section we looked at:

- the two points of view – society's need for control versus an individual's cry for help

- intensionality – the capacity to see another person's point of view

- the need to set aside our own reality

- the possibility of calling on our own experience, such as with temper tantrums

- the benefits of knowing what ASD feels like as well as knowing what it is

- the value of an empathetic approach

- sources of information about 'feelings'.

Section 2

'IS HE ONE OF US?'
The consensus of acceptable response

Whether we have impaired faculties or not, each one of us carries round a different version of 'reality' – our own point of view of the world we inhabit. The way I see things is the outcome of what I inherited from my parents, plus the whole pick-and-mix pattern of my experience and the unique way these two have interacted. The way that I react to particular circumstances is largely, if not wholly, determined by how my brain assesses the current situation in the light of previous experience. However, this assessment is also dependent on how well my senses are functioning and, even if they are functioning correctly, whether their intake is being properly processed.

Although we all have different 'realities', most of us operate within the consensus of acceptable response. We identify with people who are, by our standards, predictable – we know roughly how they will respond and are surprised and put out if they react in an unexpected way. The phrase 'Is he one of us?' encapsulates this idea. We form social, political and cultural groups on the basis of what we have in common. Conversely, we exclude those we find unpredictable.

Impairment and disability, by definition, may cause separation from the norm of experience. Although we all inhabit the same world, if my senses are impaired, my perception of what others experience may be not just a different viewpoint, I may be looking at the landscape through a totally different lens – and one that is physically damaged. For example, I may be limited by sensory deficits such as impaired vision or hearing. I may find it difficult to follow what people are saying and be 'slow on the uptake'. However, whatever the limitations of my sensory intake, or the difficulties I have in processing it, I am still a human being. Although my perception may be different, the world itself is just as much mine as yours.

Detaching ourselves from our own vision

Those of us who are working with people who are disabled often find it extremely difficult to put aside our own reality and always remember that John, for example, has tunnel vision and cannot see any signs that we make to him outside his visual field. However much we *know* what his difficulty is, in day-to-day interaction our brains may persist in superimposing our version of reality on his, so that we are unable to make the necessary imaginative leap to see the world through his restricted eyes. There is no tube in front of his eyes to remind us. Sometimes he responds and sometimes he cannot, and it is easy for us, making judgements from our standpoint, to see him as lazy, or worse, as stubborn (he will not). From where we stand, we may feel he is deliberately trying to manipulate us, to 'wind us up'. In fact, few people with severe impairments are manipulative. Although it may appear to us, from our viewpoint, that they are being so, most of their responses are instinctive rather than calculated. The blindness is ours and is the result of us projecting onto a person our sensory version of the world. It cripples our freedom to ask the crucial question, *Why?*, 'Why is it that John will happily respond sometimes and at others is completely uninterested?'

We may feel that this is very obvious but, in one form or another, this projection of our own sensory experiences onto the people we work with is a very easy trap to fall into. For example, a member of a support team may be berated because she has allowed her key-person to be mildly untidy, regardless of the fact that the house belongs to that individual. The team leader carries blueprints which are overly concerned with tidiness. She cannot distinguish between the restrictive blueprints which she carries from her own upbringing and the need to empower the individual. Her feelings of how the world 'ought' to be override her understanding of a situation where it is more important for the person to feel at home than to live in a 'super-tidy' environment.

I have laboured this point because it is crucial that we learn to detach ourselves from our own vision of what 'ought' to be in favour of what will most empower the individual concerned. This also applies to particular methods of working. Faced with a difficult scenario, it can be easy to cling to a specific approach in the teeth of evidence that it is not working, sometimes for years at a time. Yet if we think about intractable issues in a creative manner, we have the opportunity to come up with new and possibly more effective ways of getting close to an individual.

The barriers of language

We often reinforce our one-sided view by using language which is biased in favour of confrontation. We talk about 'challenging' behaviour, a word which immediately sets up expectations and resonances of opposition. If we look at the associated words in a thesaurus, we find 'provocative', 'exciting', 'rousing', 'stimulating', 'galvanising' and 'defiant', next door to 'incitive' and 'inflammatory'. In other words, we associate the word 'challenging' with processes which involve an adrenaline 'high' and not with calm. This is no way to prepare ourselves to engage with someone whose behaviour may be the outcome of inner disorientation and distress.

We may actually approach our work in the frame of mind of 'us' and 'them', so that no matter how much we consciously intend to take an approach based on sharing and equality and empowerment, we are being master-minded by ideas of control and separation. We set ourselves apart so that we can 'manage' and 'contain' behaviours, isolating them by using such terms as 'targeting' in a way that sets us up as 'victims' and does not recognise the opportunity presented for interaction. Similarly, we talk about 'attention seeking' in a way that does not address an individual's overwhelming need, for whatever reason, for contact.

This emotive and adversarial language focuses on the problems that a person presents rather than the difficulties they face. In some cases, the language may be positively misleading. For example, if we say that someone is 'selectively deaf', the immediate implication is that the behaviour is of their voluntary choosing. Similarly, we may speak of a person with ASD who will not move as 'posing', when in fact what they are probably experiencing is a failure of the processing system which leads to an uncoupling of the motor system. They are *unable* to move. (As discussed in **Section 4**, this may be one of the consequences of emotional overloading.[4] The immobility is not purposeful, but a form of evasive action devised by the brain in order to protect a person from the pain experienced in the process of fragmentation, which is brought on in response to 'feeling' the nervous system cannot handle. But if we see it from our own viewpoint, it makes it difficult for us to search for a creative way to move through their particular emotional difficulties.)

Clinical language helps us to analyse and contain situations we may find frightening or bizarre, but at the same time it separates us further from the person whose behaviour makes it difficult for us to be with them. For example, the word 'maladaptive' expresses *our* perspective; we see the behaviour from *our* point of view. We box ourselves in and are unable to take account of the psychological or perceptual obstacles and the whole raft of neurobiological discontinuities and distortions which may be part of a person's daily life (such as the variety of hypersensitivities and sensory distortions that people with ASD experience). Our responses become reactive rather than therapeutic. The more we can clarify both the therapeutic and neurobiological possibilities, the more likely we are to be able to assist the person we are trying to help.

The benefits of a more open approach

To illustrate the possibilities of a more open approach, I should like to return to the first of the three questions presented in the introduction: 'Would I agree that one should ignore undesirable social behaviour?'

The speaker described how he had had to face a daily barrage of name-calling for several months. I asked him whether he felt that ignoring the barrage had proved effective and he replied that it had not. Yet the same ritual was still being played out. Because the approach which was being taken (ignoring unacceptable social behaviour) was received wisdom – a respectable and well tested strategy – it was difficult to accept that in this instance, it was not proving effective.

We have to assume that this individual wanted to communicate but was unable to do so appropriately. It is probable that his pay-off was not the negative reaction (ignoring it) that he was getting from the person he was tormenting; almost certainly, at some earlier stage, he had raised a laugh from a third party. He wanted that positive and inclusive input again – it made him feel good. But he was going about it the wrong way. The way out of this type of impasse is not to continue giving the negative input of turning away to distance oneself, but to turn the interaction round so that the person feels included. Recalling some work I had done in a similar situation, I suggested it might work better if he gave the individual in question a big grin, agreeing and, saying something such as, 'Yeah, just my bad luck to be a… [whatever it is].'

In the similar situation, my 'holding' of a young man's inability to communicate in an acceptable way with older women, for whatever reason, was completely effective. It unblocked the impediment to communication and we became good friends. Had I clung to the idea that I should not tolerate such rudeness, we should never have moved beyond our mutual separation.

In his contribution to the book *Challenging Behaviour*, Emblem says,

> *'I have come to realise the limitations of ignoring the bad and rewarding the good.*
> *If you are really good (in the sense of skilled at your job), you can accept the bad*
> *and use it for good.'* [5]

The second question which was a starting point for this book, about whether we should be training people to take responsibility, hinges on the word 'train'. In the sense that it was asked, 'training' is about power: I decide what someone shall learn and I arrange a programme to ensure that they do so. It is not about empowerment, which helps the person to understand what is going on and motivates them to want to take part.

You Don't Know What It's Like

(A history that illustrates this, and the possible use of images that resonate for a person, is that of Mary in **Section 8**).

Similarly, the third question, about punishment and reward, is also about control. Although the intention may be benign, the effect is separation. I hope that it will become apparent throughout this book that such an approach makes it very difficult for us to ask such vital questions as:

● What is happening in this person's brain that leads them to behave like this?

● What can I do to support them?

● Is the strategy we are using working for this person?

We have to be non-judgemental. We should not be thinking about what people *ought* to be doing but what they *are* doing and what it is telling us.

Summary

Suggestions for support staff in this section include:

● avoid stereotyping and labelling

● move beyond mutual separation

● if possible, accept 'bad' behaviour and use it for good.

Section 3

'I KNOW WHAT I'M DOING'
Repetitive behaviours

At present, support staff are not always clear about why they are being asked to pursue particular programmes, especially some of those associated with people with ASD. It is easy to say, 'Oh he's autistic, therefore we work with him in such and such a way,' without knowing exactly what is going on in that individual's life and thus missing the urgency of a particular strategy.

What is it that Brenda is doing, for example, when she spends her days endlessly drawing houses – three windows and a door, terrace after terrace, street after street? Or when Jane draws tigers, always the same, endlessly stalking across the paper, wild faces turned towards the onlooker? It is easy to label this as repetitive, compulsive, fixated or stereotypic behaviour and dismiss it. From our point of view, this behaviour is a barrier to communication; it may make it extremely difficult for us to get in touch with a person. Not only do they ignore us in favour of their chosen activity, but they may also become extremely upset if we try to interrupt.

The degree of attachment to a fixation was brought home to me by Ed, a child who stored leaves in boxes. When the lawnmower drove through a pile of leaves, he rushed past distraught, shouting 'they are cutting my friends, they are killing all my friends.'

However, if we could learn more about such behaviour and understand something about what people are getting out of it, we might be able to use that understanding to get closer to them and work with them more effectively. To do this, we need to look at what able people with ASD say about what repetition does for them and why they need it.

The comfort of repetition

In her interesting and useful book *Nobody Nowhere*, Williams describes the onset and growth of her fascination with coloured specks in the air, how she first noticed them in dreams and how she gradually began to see them floating everywhere. She tells us how she focused on them and how doing so became her overriding occupation to the extent that she learned to exclude people in order to pursue them. She says that she was happy when she was with her spots and resisted being 'dragged back to understanding' when people spoke to her. As she grew older, she became afraid. She collected bits of coloured scraps and held them tightly, 'so she could fall asleep securely'.[6]

Some people suggest that Williams' ASD is atypical, sufficiently unusual to make it difficult to generalise from her insights. As discussed in *Person to Person*, in practice I have always found it helpful to build on her experience, even when working with people who are low-functioning or whose ASD is genuinely linked to severe learning impairment.

Donna Williams is an exceptional human being, exceptional in the degree to which she has been able to reflect on her condition and make her insight available, unique in the depth to which she has explored how she feels. Because we find people with ASD so difficult to reach, it is easy to assume that they do not have access to the subtle world of feeling. From our standpoint of an ability to exchange, most people with ASD do not appear to experience feelings because they do not show them to us. As we shall see, this is because they find the world they live in too threatening in sensory terms. In practice, however, many are able to cope with reciprocal interchange of emotion if we work with them inside the secure world of their stereotype where they do not feel threatened.

Williams has made it possible for us to follow her into her world by her 'inside-out' approach, as she calls it.[7] In her film, *Jam-Jar*, she uses metaphor to lead us through experiences which are acutely personal but also universal. Her coloured specks have become a jar of glass beads which sparkle in the light. She groups them by their similarities to show how they are related. She is a different bead and alone. With a breathtaking leap of imagination, she breaks out of her isolation by becoming 'a traveller who likes to visit'. Her body language changes and she laughs in her new freedom. This contrasts very strongly with a later sequence in the film, where she is playing with the beads and where, although she may be partially in control of this 'as demonstration', she gets caught up in the game she is playing – in her inner world. Her voice is that of a child who is lost in a game, for whom the game has taken over. The inner world is all that there is.

The fixation that Williams describes so clearly is visual – and it emerges that she is hyper-sensitive to vision.[6] What she was looking at as a child was particles in the air – perhaps as we should see motes in a dusty sunbeam – but the range of sources that can be used repetitively is endless, from innate self-stimulation through touch, sound and vision, to complicated rituals involving objects and activities from the outside world. Jenny, for example, endlessly runs small pebbles through her hands. It is not a question of intelligence. Professor Temple Grandin, who has described her ASD in a number of books and interviews, speaks of her own fixation with running grains of sand through her hand.[8]

Thérèse Jolliffe says:

> 'Up to the age of seven or eight, I spent hours enjoying running my fingers over and scratching on the edge of my pillowcase which had embroidery around it. I still do this now with different surfaces, especially if they feel good and make a small sound.'[9]

Sometimes it is hard to identify the activities on which people are focusing. They may be hidden, such as digging fingernails into the palm of a clenched hand, or so unremarkable that we would discount them, such as a breathing rhythm. They may be what we would regard as socially unacceptable, such as picking dandruff from the head and looking at the white flecks, or they may be uncomfortable sounds such as teeth grinding which we ignore. However, laying aside their exact origin and the exact form that the repetitions take, the most direct clue as to what an individual is getting out of them appears in Sian Barron's account of his childhood autism. He says:

> 'I loved repetition. Every time I turned a light on, I knew what would happen. It gave me a wonderful sense of security because it was exactly the same each time.'[10]

For those of us not in his position, this sounds strange. However, I have highlighted this because it is extremely important and I shall be referring to it again in this book (and do constantly when I am working and teaching.) While we need to explore the role of repetitive behaviours in producing endorphins in the brain which reduce the pain that is the outcome of sensory fragmentation (see **Section 16**), for now it is crucial to remember that when a person is using stereotypic behaviour, in a world of sensory chaos, **they know what they are doing**.

We should find doing the same thing, over and over again, boring. In order to see what is going on, we need to switch out of our own reality and move into the sensory world that a person with ASD is trying to process. We need to see why it is that a person should have an overwhelming need for repetition and security to the extent that they may become deeply disturbed if attempts are made to move them out of the world they are locked into. Why, when we can look round and see and hear and feel and understand our experiences (what is going on for us), and when there is nothing wrong with Sian's senses (he could see, hear and feel normally), why does he say that he found it comforting *to know what was going on in his world?* What is it that is so different and threatening for Sian about the world we share with him?

Summary

Suggestions in this section include:

- look carefully and non-judgementally at what a person is doing, even if it has no immediate significance or seems bizarre

- ask yourself what they are getting out of their behaviour

- think about stereotypic and repetitive behaviours in terms of security in a world that does not make sense.

Section 4

'A WHOLE LOT OF CONFUSED JUMBLES'
What ASD 'feels' like

Many of us have been taught to think about ASD in terms of a triad of impairments:

1 a deficit in language and communication

2 a deficit in ability to form social relationships

3 an impairment of the capacity to think flexibly and use imagination.

This is our point of view, a diagnosis which tells us how people with ASD appear to us – what to expect – but it doesn't tell us much about how such people feel, how they experience reality. There is a gap between how we as carers experience the difficulties ASD presents us with and what it is that people with ASD and other difficult behaviours are living through.

In recent years a number of people have written and spoken eloquently about how they experience autism – what it is like for them. Considering the extraordinary breadth of manifestation of autism, their accounts paint a very consistent picture. Of course, the authors are self-selected, being high-functioning and able to write, but in practice, even from this narrow base, it has proved extremely helpful to think about what they are saying when working with less able people. Unfortunately, their accounts are rather scattered so it seems useful to draw some of them together for the benefit of those who do not have access to all of them.

Sensory overload

This is Lindsey Weeks, speaking on a radio programme about his childhood:

> 'I'd always had problems with getting a sort of coherency out of the world unless
> I could be in somewhere I was very familiar with like my room, in my space,
> because it's very easy in autism for the world to fragment under pressure.

> 'If I get a lot of sensory overload then I just shut down ... you get what's known
> as fragmentation ... it gets really weird, like being tuned into forty TV channels at once.

> 'You just get this whole overload of sensory impressions – if you get that when you're four,
> it's total panic. You're going to run full tilt into a wall or into the traffic, anything to stop
> the sensory overload happening because I'd much rather have pain...it's one overriding
> sensation rather than getting a whole lot of confused jumbles. When you're adult it's
> freaky enough, but when you're a kid it's really bad.'

And again:

> 'If your senses start to become fragmented or if you start to feel reality slipping away from
> you, you want to focus on something. Sometimes they don't focus exclusively on pain like
> smashing into a brick wall, it's just as easy to flick a light on and off very rapidly, like
> strobe lights at a disco and you just focus on that.' [11]

Thérèse Jolliffe says:

> 'The world of the non-verbal person with autism is chaotic and confusing. A low-functioning
> adult who is not toilet-trained may be living in a completely disordered sensory world.
> It is likely that they have no idea of their body boundaries and that sights, senses and
> touch are all mixed together. It must be like seeing the world through a kaleidoscope
> and trying to listen to a radio station that is jammed with static and has a faulty volume
> control all at once.' [9]

How can we possibly put ourselves in this position? Searching for an image which
meets the above descriptions, I should like to borrow the phrase, 'landscapes without
landmarks', used by Grant in the completely different context of dementia.[12] In ASD,
it is not that the landmarks are being eroded or erased as they are in dementia (and in
the case of profound disability, they may have never been there). Rather, the description
fits because a person's sensory perceptions of existing landmarks are being progressively
shredded so that they are unrecognisable. Under this bombardment, the floating bits

merely add to confusion as the individual gropes not only for destination but also for starting point – where they are now.

> **JILLY bangs her head on a particular shape of carpet pattern when she is overloaded, holding on to the one piece of coherent reality she can identify.**

It is clear that what we are looking at is a battleground, not only with the physical senses but also with tumultuous emotional experience – what Williams calls 'a love-hate relationship with oneself'.[7] A colleague has remarked that the emotions can be completely labile: *'You reach out for sorrow and get despair.'* [13]

A struggle is in progress between the order that we take for granted in our world and disintegration. Survival is the issue and victory is by no means assured.

According to Grandin, whereas low-functioning people may not understand what is said to them and therefore be unable to reply, high-functioning people with ASD may grasp what is said to them but still be unable to organise a response. She speaks of the appalling frustration this caused her.[14] Similarly, Jolliffe says:

> *'Sometimes when I really need to speak and can't, the frustration is terrible. I want to kick out at people and objects, throw things, rip them and break them and occasionally to scream.'* [9]

Trying to process sensory intake seems to be like a conveyor belt going faster and faster. Williams says:

> *'I keep running, running, running, trying to keep up.'* [7]

It helps if we use the model of a bottleneck. The visual images, sounds and touches come in undistorted, but are unable to pass through the narrowing neck. The pressure builds up and the images fragment.

We, the outsiders, can get a little idea of the extraordinary lengths to which the human spirit will go to bring order into chaos when the question we ask of a person with ASD today is answered perfectly tomorrow. For the person with ASD, it has taken that long to process the reply. We dismiss the endeavour which keeps going for that length of time, battling to assemble the fragments into a pattern, because we cannot see it. The only evidence we have of the heroic struggle is that the person we want to talk to takes an irritatingly long time to respond. We see it from our viewpoint and the gulf between our world and theirs widens.

The first thing we need to understand is that **the most likely explanation for an outburst in a person with ASD is that they are unable to cope with the sensory overload they are experiencing**. They are not 'just being difficult'.

The senses

Distortions and break-up of incoming stimuli can occur in any of the senses and, according to Gillingham, are mainly related to hypersensitivities; for example, a person may find certain sounds acutely painful.[15] Again, we can get some idea of what they are experiencing from their accounts.

Seeing is difficult. Objects tend to jump around and slide away. The brain focuses on particular detail rather than on the whole. Williams says:

> 'I never see the whole. If I see the leaves, I don't see the tree.' [16]

In the video *A is for Autism* (Arnall & Peters, 1992) a small boy says :

> 'It is difficult for me to concentrate on things, particularly if they are important. The more important they are, the more they seem to slide away.'[17]

We know now that this type of visual disturbance, which is the effect of scotopic sensitivity, can sometimes be markedly reduced by wearing tinted lenses. Williams gives accounts of the beneficial effects of Irlen lenses.[18]

I had wrongly assumed that the difficulties of testing would make it impossible to work in a similar way with people with autism who also had very severe behavioural or learning disabilities – until recently, as the following history describes:

JAKE clearly has severe learning disabilities as well as ASD. He sat with his head down and eyes screwed up in a way that suggested he found vision difficult. When staff tried a pair of green lenses on, he pushed them away. But when they followed this with pink lenses, he kept them on, his head came up and he started to look round the room in an interested way. This reaction has now been noted with a number of clients.

It is important to realise that the actual colour that works to correct this dysfunction (scotopic sensitivity) can be very specific and needs testing as it differs from individual to individual. The suggestion is that individuals require a particular frequency to adjust the input so that it is more in synchronisation with the capacity to process. This may mean speeding up or slowing down the input, so different and very specific colours are required to correct the dysfunction of each individual. The work described above does not constitute a test for scotopic sensitivity, it was only an indication of possibility which has to be followed by a professional test.

Regarding the visual dysfunctions experienced by some people with ASD, there is no guarantee of continuity. As a colleague put it:

'Mummy in a red dress can be a different person to Mummy in a blue dress.'

Also, dimensions can shift. A room that appears to be of normal size one minute can collapse the next. This is a life-threatening scenario. Almost all childhood accounts of people with autism speak of terror or of terrifying situations. It is not surprising that they react with such desperation, as Jolliffe says:

'I am frightened of so many things that can be seen: people, particularly faces, very bright lights, large machines and buildings that are unfamiliar, my own shadow, the dark bridges, rivers, canals and the sea.' [9]

One of the most difficult things is to look at people. Williams describes eye contact as acutely painful[6] and Jolliffe says:

'People do not appreciate how unbearably difficult it is to look at people. It is terribly frightening.' [9]

We get the same story when we look at touch and sound. Weeks says:

'I don't particularly like being touched, touch is not pleasant for me at all, unless I'm warned in advance that I'm going to experience this sensation. Otherwise, I don't like it.' [11]

Speaking of his childhood, he says:

'People were touching me and pulling me around like they do with all kids and I was reacting badly to it.' [11]

Grandin, who is hypersensitive to touch, says that light touch is like a cattle prod which fires off every nerve in her body. She may be able to feel the scratch of uncomfortable clothes a fortnight later. On the other hand, deep pressure may be helpful. In her book, *Emergence Labelled Autistic* she describes how, when she was quite young, she built herself a pressure machine which helped her to desensitise her skin.[8]

Many sounds, particularly high-frequency sounds, are extremely painful and frightening. Again, we may have a life-threatening situation, when a toilet being flushed may sound like an express train about to run one over. But the painful sounds may also be very small, for example, the click of a ballpoint pen. Voices at normal level may hurt. In *Person to Person*, it was noted how the incidence of Ben's attacks on people dropped markedly when support staff deliberately spoke in very soft voices.*

People and emotional overload

According to Williams, it is not just sensory information from the outside world that can cause overload, but also the bodily feelings generated by emotional contact which may be perceived as hostile. The brain just can't process the information fast enough and people have problems keeping up. Internal physical feelings become disconnected from the events that set them off. Instead of giving emotional information the feelings may come in terrifying gusts which are unrelated (in time) to their inception. Williams says:

> 'Where meaning and significance connect so rarely in the context that provokes them, the emotional feelings that these cause may be felt extremely, yet out of context. Without comprehension to make sense of them, the effect on the body may be so extreme that it is too much for the body to sustain.'[4]

She goes on to describe how intense, out-of-control physical sensations may be wrongly perceived as danger and an attack on the body:

> 'an adrenaline rush puts the body on hyper-alert.'[4]

To defend themselves, people may attack others or self-injure. The brain may become dissociated – switch to auto-pilot; there may be a systems shut-down of communication and/or movement, or there may be hypersensitivity. If the brain learns that emotional experience causes overload, this can lead to avoidance which becomes an integral part of a person's identity. In an effort to cut down on emotional overload, the brain may cut off from the motor system, so that the person freezes and is unable to move.[4]

---

* For further extensive information and examples of hypersensitivity, see Gillingham.[15]

You Don't Know What It's Like

Sometimes a person can be helped out of this evasive action by powerful but non-threatening visual 'clues'. Since the person is frozen, it is important to place these clues squarely within their visual field – they must be able to see them without moving.

> **BETH, who has ASD, gets locked into a 'loop' of laughing which is persistent. It can go on for twenty minutes and has nothing to do with finding a situation funny. Her hands and head are tilted at the ceiling. She likes coffee. Offering her coffee and showing her a mug does nothing until this is placed above her head in front of her eyes so she can clearly see it. She comes out of the loop at once and accepts the drink.**
>
> It seems possible that, in order to be successful, the 'clue' has to be presented through a channel other than that which is blocked. In Beth's case, although she can hear, her hearing does not appear to be operational when she is offered coffee which is out of her line of sight. This does not mean she does not want it. As soon as the coffee is put where she can see it, she can take on board what is on offer through her unblocked sense of vision, so she stops at once. She has made the move, from the inner world she was locked into, back to the outside world.

The need for clues may be so great that a person is unable to proceed until they have actually seen someone else do an activity. Even 'objects of reference' (objects which are an integral part of an activity used as prompts) are not enough, the person must have a role model so that they can copy the whole sequence of the activity.

> **JEFF is unable to comply when his keyworker shows him a slice of bread and points to the toaster. Eventually his keyworker tires of waiting and puts his own slice in. Immediately Jeff puts his in. He is not unwilling but unable to make the necessary movements until he has a behavioural template to copy.**

Sometimes the effect of shut-down may be less severe. The person starts activities but comes to a halt and stands waiting for help. This is sometimes interpreted as laziness but it is not. The person needs visual clues to re-establish the connection between the brain and the motor system.

Thérèse Jolliffe explains how the complexity of increasing stimulation affects her:

> *'Objects are frightening. Moving objects are harder to cope with because of the added complexity of movement. Moving objects which also make a noise are even harder – you*

have to try to take in the sight, movement and further complexity of noise. People are the hardest of all to understand because, not only do you have to try to cope with the problem of just seeing them, they move about when you are not expecting them to, they make various noises and, along with this, they place all sorts of demands on you which are just impossible to understand.' [9]

Warburton says:

'I like reading about inanimate objects – human beings are too complex. I never know how to behave when they are around. I feel like a foreigner in an alien world except when I'm on my own.' [19]

Eye contact is a particular problem. In *Person to Person* I describe the history of Paula who is extremely disturbed and has frequent outbursts against people and property. However, she becomes able to make close physical contact if I look away while I speak to her. She clearly enjoys this occasion and also other interactions which use an impersonal approach.

If people are avoiding eye-contact, it is better to look away when talking to them and it may also help to use indirect speech. This makes it much easier to for them to respond and interact; it takes off the personal pressure which leads to stress so that they can process what is going on more easily.

A more able person may prefer to write rather than speak. Weeks explains:

'Writing is my preferred method of communicating with the world…because it's impersonal. I don't have to have anything to do with the person I'm writing to, I can express myself better, the pressure is off. Sitting here talking to you, you're a presence…you're there. [It feels like] another person invading my world.' [11]

A person with ASD may not even understand their connection with other people. Jolliffe says:

'I cannot remember ever thinking about where my mother, father, brother and sister were, they did not seem to concern me. I did not realise they were people and that people were supposed to be important.' [9]

While Barron remembers:

'I didn't know what people were for.' [10]

For us, this is an extraordinary statement with its implication that it is possible to pass through at least part of one's life in a state that is totally disconnected from other human beings. This is an aloneness which is beyond our comprehension.

A sense of self

We can also consider the question of how people with ASD perceive themselves. Some of the accounts of high-functioning people bear witness to a strong sense of self and of themselves as separate from others. Weeks realised other people were different but assumed he had got it right and they were all wrong.[11] Williams says it was late in her life that she realised that others had a different perception to hers.[16] Weeks says that he likes himself as he is and would not wish to change and Grandin agrees:

> 'If I could snap my fingers and be non-autistic, I would not – because I wouldn't be me. Autism is part of who I am.' [14]

In a particularly moving interview, Williams, who also likes herself, expresses her sorrow at being unable to use all her senses in an integrated way; that is, process all of them simultaneously.[16]

It is probably not helpful to try to generalise, as people with ASD have as wide a range of experience as those outside it. However, what we can say is that they may have a very poor sense of boundary which affects their sense of who and where they are. For example, Williams describes how she spent two years trying to shake off a hand that she did not realise was hers. It was a floating object in front of her. This seems to have been because her brain, in an effort to cope with more sensory input than it could handle, had learned to switch off either 'seeing' or 'feeling'. She calls it 'going into mono' and when she is in this state, she only processes one of these senses at a time. As she only saw or felt but never did both at the same time, she never got the idea of organic connection between her hand and the rest of her.[4]

Some confusion arises from how we define 'self' – whether we define it in terms of physical limits, 'where my skin ends', or as my inner feeling of myself, knowing 'who' rather than 'what' I am. They are not the same thing. For example, I know who I am – and should I be unfortunate enough to lose an arm, I should still be that same self. But I might well be wrong about my boundaries since my phantom limb might be giving me incorrect information about its presence. Even for those of us without ASD, our sense of boundary can be very elastic. If I am in my car, it becomes part of me in a sense, and the boundary of myself is my wheels on the road. With ASD, you may have no idea of which bits of yourself are you and what belong to other people. This can be intensely invasive and it is not surprising that so many such people deliberately seek solitude.

Thérèse Jolliffe says:

> *'Reality to an autistic person is a confusing, interacting mass of events, people, places, sounds and sights. There seem to be no boundaries, order or meaning to anything. **A large part of my life is spent trying to work out the pattern behind everything.**'* [9]

It is possible to speculate that, in the future, we shall view failure to perceive boundaries (and, where it arises, to have a clear sense of self) purely as the outcome of dysfunctional processing of sensory intake. Sometimes this can, potentially at least, be partly corrected by use of Irlen lenses where the user finds them physically acceptable. A positive physical reaction has been strongly marked, even in people with severe behavioural difficulties or who have severe learning disabilities in addition to their autism.

> **RICHARD, who has ASD, has also been labelled as showing psychotic behaviour (and has been severely withdrawn as well as challenging). When he starts walking round with a smile on his face and looking at everything in a new and interested way, one can only speculate at the life-changing relief he is experiencing. Before wearing his tinted lenses, he would frequently start an activity and then come to a halt, needing someone to show him how to complete it. Although it is only two months since he received his new lenses, it appears that he can now usually complete tasks. He is much more relaxed and interested in his surroundings.**

> **When she first received her new maroon coloured lenses, IVY took them off and put them on frequently but she now wears them much of the time. She decides when she wants them on or not. (It is as if at first she needed to compare her new world with her old.) Ivy is now calmer and spends much of her time with her head up looking round instead of looking down at her fingers as before.**

Time and routine

In the world of sensory confusion, there is another flickering dimension to contend with, that of time. In her film, *Jam-Jar*, Williams says:

> *'I was totally caught up in every moment. I never ever got the whole picture of me, I never got the whole picture of who I was yesterday, who I am today, where I am going tomorrow. I never got the whole picture of even a whole day or who anyone was in relation to anybody else and so that is a huge turmoil inside of a person.'* [7]

If we consider this, we can begin to see why it is that people with ASD find change in routine so difficult to handle. In the middle of incoherency, they sometimes just about grasp a pattern. All their energy is focused on this, trying to hold it together and then suddenly, meaning slips away and they are plunged back into chaos. The anticipated picture that they have pieced together in their mind does not marry with the visual image of the situation they find themselves in so they become stressed. No wonder people react as though to catastrophe – in their sphere of perception this is exactly what they are experiencing. As Lindsey Weeks puts it:

> 'Autistic people like sameness, simply because they know what's coming next, things are more coherent. I liked [as a child] to wake up and know what was going to happen to me on that day as far as possible – otherwise there were tantrums for them.' [11]

The sanctuary

In this kaleidoscope world, we begin to see why people with ASD develop rituals which may appear bizarre to us, but which for them are refuges, safe places where they feel they are in control.

Is such an approach really so foreign to us? If we look back at our childhood behaviour, we may see snatched pleasure or security derived from activities such as running a finger over corrugations or a stick along railings, counting endlessly to the point where counting becomes obligatory (otherwise something dreadful will happen). We play games which ritualise our fantasies – 'Lines and Squares', hopping from one paving stone to the next, never treading on a line or the horror will get us, whatever its form. We daydream, going off into worlds of clicks and hums and repetitive words. A child whose family circumstances entailed constant house moves, licked the walls of her room so that it would be safely there for her to return to, ensuring its permanence.

What difference is there between this behaviour and that of Ray, who has to lick every lamp-post he passes? He is also looking for permanence in the turmoil of his chaotic experience. The child was lucky. Her background contained enough stability for her to grow through her uncertainty but Ray's environment continued to behave in an unpredictable manner. He found it comforting, and later compulsory, to continue his rituals in order to hold himself together.

For the person with ASD, it seems that these behaviours, whatever their origin, do represent security. They are signals the brain gives itself which do not break up and therefore present no threat – in the midst of chaos they are reassuring and calming.

The person knows what is happening when they are involved in them. We can think of them as hard-wired into the brain. As Jolliffe says:

'What other people call 'odd' hand movements and grimaces are not meant to annoy, they give a sense of control, safety and pleasure.' [9]

After describing the extremely painful sensation of fragmentation, Weeks goes on to talk about an autistic person's fascination with strobe lights, how, at a disco amid all the noise:

'They just watch the strobe lights – really cool – in the middle of the whole thing – it just coheres.' [11]

If we look back at Williams' account of her fixation with specks of light (**Section 3**), we see that not only does the behaviour cut out painful input, it also becomes interesting in itself so that all attention becomes focused on it. Some people cut out altogether. Jolliffe also says she used to pull a big blanket over her head as it made her feel safer.[9]

In her moving poem, *Nobody Nowhere*, Williams tells us how lonely it can be:

'And the world can grow cold in the depths of your soul
When you think nothing can hurt you until it's too late.' [6]

From our standpoint, because they are unable to share their feelings, we say that people with ASD do not experience them. Jolliffe would disagree – describing her own feelings she says:

'People with autism can be lonely and can love.' [9]

My own experience of working with people with ASD is that they almost always respond warmly and frequently show affection if one can speak to them in a language that their brain recognises as non-threatening, one that is based on the signals they give to themselves. This is illustrated in the following history:

I am asked to find a way of working with VERA who has severe ASD. This is the first time we have met. She finds people difficult, particularly strangers. She has a number of ways of 'cutting out'.

She puts her hand over her face.
She puts her fingers in her ears.
She puts your hand over her face.
She turns her back on you.
She becomes totally absorbed in rustling and folding a crisp bag, examining its shiny surfaces.

I ask if I may sit next to her, pointing to myself and then the sofa beside her. She gives me a fractional nod of agreement. When I sit down, she turns her back and starts to fold her crisp bag but does not get up and move away. Moving into her language, I also start to play with a crisp bag. She can hear its characteristic rustle although she is not looking at me. After a few minutes, she looks over her shoulder. We start a conversation with each other – she rattles her crisp bag and I follow. Suddenly she flings herself across my lap and lies there, looking straight up at me and laughing as we talk to each other. This interaction goes on for about 20 minutes and ends when she loses my attention as I start talking to support staff about what we are doing. She sits up and turns away from me. I accept this, say goodbye and leave her.

VERA, who cannot bear people, particularly strangers, is perfectly able to let me know that she enjoys my company when I use 'her' language. It does not threaten her with overload and fragmentation and she and I are able to share our pleasure in each other.

You Don't Know What It's Like

Summary

What is it like to live in a landscape without signposts? Using the accounts of high-functioning people with ASD, it seems that they are experiencing the world we share in a different and often extremely frightening way:

- they may be unable to cope with the sensory overload
- they may be unable to handle feelings which become detached from events
- they probably have no clear sense of boundary or of time
- overload and fragmentation may lead to outbursts.

We can reach them in a non-threatening way if we use their language.

Section 5

'WHEN'S THE BUS COMING?'
The uncertainty of time

How does it feel to live in a world governed by time and yet not be able to understand its dimensions? The idea of 'time' is part of our life-support system and we take it for granted. As we grow up, learning to tell the time is a landmark on the journey from dependence to independence. From that point on we can, at least potentially, organise our lives. We have learned that events happen in order and that there are intervals between them. We know what will happen and when – and we can predict what will happen in the future. Using time as a platform, we can take an overview – we are both attached to and participant in our lives.

Once we are aware of time, it is very difficult for us to visualise what life would be like without it. We cannot take it away and, although it is ever-present and we refer to it constantly, we hardly give a thought to it. Like the air we breathe, we take it for granted. It is hard for us to be aware of the tensions and anxieties that accompany an absence of this structure.

If we now put ourselves in the position of those for whom time is incomprehensible, we are not able to grasp the length of the intervals, although the same pressures are present for us as for the people in the world who *do* understand time. We may know, for example, that we have to catch the bus home – we shall be in trouble if we do not; someone will be cross with us or we will have to wait, or walk and maybe lose our way. Our life fills up with threatening unknowns. Double bind.

We learn clues to attach to our departure: maybe we have grasped the sequence and know our departure is after coffee, but we do not know how long after. We misread this clue and go and stand by the door with our coats as soon as tea-break is over, focusing on the bus coming. Better safe than sorry. Someone pushes past. Interrupting our theme

You Don't Know What It's Like

disturbs us and throws us into uncertainty, underscoring our anxiety. We hit out, or hit ourselves.

This description of the anxiety that surrounds time is one that most readers will be familiar with in one form or another. It is easy enough to recognise: endless questions about who is coming when, or what is going to happen. We cannot answer these questions adequately because it is not possible for the enquirer to attach meaning to our reply – even if they can repeat it themselves, our words are sounds, empty of content.

The only way we can really appreciate the emotional impact of what it feels like to not understand the structure of time is to place ourselves in a situation with which we are probably all familiar: in this case, it is not that there is no structure, but that the structure as we know it fails. Let us suppose that we have invited our friend Nick to come over tomorrow afternoon. We predict with reasonable certainty that he will turn up after lunch. What happens if he fails to come?

We might wait a bit and then start to ask around. We telephone people we think might have seen him. Niggling worry builds up as we follow false trails. What's happened to Nick, the Nick we depend on? Has he had an accident? Our anxiety about his safety mingles with wondering about how we shall manage without him; he is part of our life-support system – that intricate web we weave round ourselves to nourish our existence. By following this scenario, we begin to understand that to live in a world which is governed by time but not to understand it, is to go through day after day constantly being topped up with anxiety about what will happen. As we can see, such anxiety can move swiftly from minor worry to panic.

A similar anxiety can be found in the lives of people who are more able but whose physical impairments prevent their taking charge of their lives.

> **TOM has cerebral palsy. He lives at home and is in a state of acute anxiety because he is not being supplied with the information he needs – no-one has thought it necessary to involve him in planning his timetable or to tell him of their decisions or even, perhaps, that these have not yet been made. As far as he can see, his day-service provision is slipping away. Assumptions have been made about his ability and preferences because his speech is not always easy to decode. However, he manages to describe how he sits at home and listens for the phone to ring from his college, to tell him what the next term's programme will be. It's all he has to do and the anxiety affects his behaviour. Once we have understood what is worrying him, he tells us that he is more confident now that we have listened to him.**

It is easy to generate anxiety and tension by failing to supply adequate information in a form that a particular individual can make sense of. Our immediate response has to be to try to diffuse the anxiety and distract the person from any disturbed behaviour. One technique which is effective in many cases is the use of non-threatening surprise in the context of intensive interaction.

> **BETH is worried about catching the bus home. Towards the end of the afternoon she starts to show this anxiety by running out to see if the bus is coming and banging her head. Once this has started, her support staff are unable to stop her – she is completely locked into her self-injurious behaviour. I suggest that they try knocking the wall in time to her banging. She is surprised that her sound and rhythm are coming from outside herself and she stops and does not restart. The internal 'loop' in which she was trapped has been broken and she is able to step out of it. She is intrigued by what is going on round her.**

However, important though it is to be able to distract the person at the time of their anxiety, *it is even more urgent to search for ways to relieve the underlying stress.*

In the history of Tom, looked at opposite, those involved have not considered the impact that anxiety about his future may have on Tom, a young man trapped in his body and unable to take charge of his life himself. In effect, failure to listen to him and failure to give him necessary information – or even to tell him that the information he needs is not available yet and give him a date when it will be – is to treat him as a child with all the vital decisions in his life being made over his head. He feels desperate and angry.

Presenting information about time

In order to be less dependent, we all need information, and it needs to be presented in a way in which we can handle it. It is perfectly possible to design 'clocks' that relate intervals directly to events. For example, one engineer designed a moving light beam to relate to pictures. Another method is to use an electric clock which has been simplified by removing the minute hand: the hour hand lines up directly with the pictures (or objects of reference if that is what is required). Kitchen timers also help people to understand intervals and the vital difference between 'now' and 'not now'. We can design various forms of timetables, as described in *Person to Person*, to assist in understanding sequences so that people know what is happening, when and, even, what is happening now.

You Don't Know What It's Like

In this respect, the educational approach of TEACCH programmes (see **Resources**, page 117) appears to be very helpful in introducing structure to children's lives. Every task is programmed and coded in such a way that the child always knows what they are doing. They can also programme in for themselves time to opt out to their safe places when they need to do so.

However, within that security, they also need to learn to develop their emotional capacity – an outcome of the approach known as Intensive Interaction. We need to use a combination of techniques: on the one hand making the ways of our world clear to people with ASD; on the other, developing their ability to relate so that, within their new security, they begin to feel safe enough to enjoy being with others. Above all, we have to put aside our certainties and recognise the uncertainties which beset those whose existence is pinned to an environment that is, for them, without structure.

Summary

We can:

- appreciate anxiety in a world where a person does not understand the intervals of time
- relieve anxiety by presenting intervals in ways that people can understand.

Section 6

'THE MAN WHO WALKED BACKWARDS'

The validity of individual logic

DAVE, who has Asperger's syndrome and occasionally has severe outbursts of disturbed behaviour, has what is seen as a baffling habit of walking backwards at times.

One school of thought is that he should be made to walk forwards. Another way to look at it is to ask what it is that he is getting out of this habit. What does it do for him? We need to remind ourselves of Donna Williams describing the turmoil in which she lives, where she never has the whole picture of where and who she is (see **Section 4**).

Putting myself in Dave's place: if I don't know where I am, I might try to backtrack, that is, retrace my steps – walk backwards to see if I could recover where I was/am. This would be logical within the framework of my distorted perception, even if it was inexplicable to an observer. Most habits are logical if they are viewed within an alternative framework. In order to see what an individual is getting out of a habit, an outsider has to assume the validity of their logic. It is not the person's reasoning which is incorrect but the premise in which it is rooted. We need to be able to backtrack with them to see where they are coming from.

Suppose I have entered Dave's world and decoded what he is doing – where does that get me? How does it help me to help Dave?

From my point of view, it is less irritating for me if I know the reason why he is doing it.

(As human beings, we tend to find it disturbing if someone is behaving in a way that seems nonsensical. It niggles us, questions our behaviour, and we feel the need to obtain conformity. We say that people will laugh at the person, but we may also be afraid of being associated with the bizarre behaviour – that we shall also be made to look silly.)

Observing Dave's behaviour through my reaction to it prevents me looking for a less coercive way of helping him. I need to see if I can reduce the stress in his life. He will then have less sensory confusion to struggle with and will therefore be more able to perceive his environment in an organised way – to have more idea of who he is and where he is at any given time.

> When Dave goes home he walks upstairs and paces up and down a long corridor. His mother says that if she calls him, he will sometimes come but sometimes mutters to himself, 'She's not going to hurry me.' He comes down when he is ready and is not upset.

What is interesting is that Dave behaves in a comparable way when he reaches his day centre. He does not come in but paces round the centre, sometimes for a considerable length of time. When he is ready, he comes in.

Taking each behaviour in isolation, it might be difficult to see what is going on. However, when put together, they suggest that when Dave, who is very able, is subject to changes, he needs time to sort out what is happening for him. He knows this and takes active steps to sort himself out before joining other people. Far from trying to hurry Dave, we need to give him space to manage himself.

Knowing that Dave, although he can read and write well, needs time to process information, staff at the centre he attends have devised a system to help him participate more fully in meetings that concern his life. Without help, Dave finds it difficult to keep up with what is being said, so an assistant sits beside him and takes notes. These are transferred to a card index system in a box. This allows him to go through the information with his assistant at his own pace at a later time and pick out anything which he wants to clarify. He also has a small box in which he can take a selection of relevant cards to a meeting. As well as this, he can help to control the agenda of future meetings by picking out and laying out in order his priorities when his affairs are discussed.[20] (Although one might think this type of difficulty relates to auditory processing, this is not necessarily always so. Visual input takes up 70% of our processing capacity and Williams says that when she wears the coloured lenses, her capacity to understand speech is improved.[18] Presumably, she has more time to focus on it when she is not struggling with overwhelming visual problems.)

When we are working with people with severe sensory complications, we must look at the whole picture and ask ourselves what it is the individual is experiencing. We need to respect the coping strategies that people have developed in order to help themselves.

For example, a woman who turns off the TV or radio when she is becoming disturbed is trying to cut down on sensory confusion – she is trying to help herself. The proper response is to try to provide her with a quiet and undemanding environment so that she can feel secure and continue to work on herself. At the same time, we can provide a way of interacting that she finds non-threatening through Intensive Interaction and activities based on her own language and preferences.

Summary

This section discussed ways of helping people with ASD:

- cope with change
- keep up with the flow of conversation.

you don't know what it's like

Section 7

'A SAFE PLACE INSIDE MYSELF'
Two worlds

One of the concepts I find helpful when thinking about behaviour, not only in relation to people with ASD, arises out of the way that Donna Williams refers to 'my world' and 'their world'. She talks about the strain of constantly having to be in 'their world'.[7] To make this distinction clearer, I shall call these the 'inner' and the 'outer' worlds.

In fact, however aware of it we are, we all live in two worlds and have an inner personal and private world. How our lives develop is at least partly dependent on how we are able to balance this inner world with the demands of the public world outside. We function best when there is a bridge between them and they inform and enrich each other. If all is not well in our public world, we may, particularly as children, retreat to our inner world, the place where we started off as infants and where our whole experience of the world was an extension of ourselves. We felt safe. Under stressful circumstances, communication between public outer and inner personal world may break down and the bridge become a drawbridge. We cannot talk to the world and it cannot talk to us. We are turned in on ourselves.

Describing her difficulties with the demands of a public world which thought she was stupid because people did not understand the difficulties she was experiencing, Williams says that all the turmoil this brought her made her decide:

'the only safe place was in myself.'[7]

> **RACHEL, who has ASD and learning difficulties, is locked in a private world where she focuses continually on rubbing her face. This makes her difficult to communicate with.**
>
> It is breakfast time. Her keyworker asks Rachel to take a spoon and stir some sugar in her cup. She goes towards the cup but keeps breaking off as her keyworker's suggestion is overridden by her compulsion to touch her cheek. She wants her breakfast and opens and closes her mouth, clearly thinking about food as she moves towards the cupboard, but her brain keeps diverting her back to 'scratch', 'touch', 'scratch' and she gets lost again. She cannot cross the bridge between the compulsion of her inner world to the 'real' outer world with its need to organise her meal, until her attention is caught by her keyworker reflecting back to her, her movements. This establishes the contact she needs with the public outside world. She is able to start preparing her breakfast.

At this stage, we need to look at what we mean when we speak of inner personal and public outer worlds, the relationship of these to unconsciousness and consciousness, and where the autistic inner personal world links in.

Inner and outer feedback

It is generally accepted that all of us, when we were infants, made the journey from an undifferentiated world (where we existed in the illusion that everything was part of us) to the outside world of reality.[21] This progress from 'me' to 'not me' Stern calls the movement from 'core self' to 'core other'.[22] The transition takes place through 'reality testing', a process whereby the child learns to relate what he or she does to the effect this has. This process is facilitated by the parent figure who confirms the infant's struggles to emerge from the insulated and isolated state. This process is often painful – Winnicott describes the assault of reality as an 'insult' (it may threaten our existence – an anxiety-provoking scenario). Winnicott goes on to point out that while our inner psychic reality is largely unconscious, the feelings that arise from it are not.[21]

For example, we may use our hand repetitively to sweep back our hair; in a world where we have a poor self-image and are not sure of ourselves, this gesture makes us feel attractive. For a millisecond we reassure ourselves, we have the feeling that we are all right. We call this activity a habit and we may not know we do it. If someone points it out to us, we feel surprised and at the same time we may feel a small flicker of shame. Our feeling of 'needing to be attractive' is exposed like a raw nerve.

Until this point, our behaviour has been beyond our control since we have not known what we were doing. Now that we have become aware of our feelings and actions, we have a choice: we can alter our behaviour or continue – but in the latter case we feel uneasy because we are now aware of our exposed position. In order to change, we need not only to know what we are doing, but we also have to address our underlying weakness. In the previous example, we cannot just stop feeling unattractive. We may need help and support to do this, otherwise, half-knowing, we may add guilt to our shame. **In order for us to take responsibility for our actions, we may need someone to help us feel good about ourselves.**

If we turn our attention back to our inner personal world, we may know what we are doing but still be at the mercy of repetitive messages from the brain which are outside our control. Even though we are semi-aware of them, they dictate what we do. We might call it a state of automated consciousness. The more we cut ourselves off from the outside world, the more vulnerable we are to compulsive processes since we no longer have external standards to verify our behaviour. (We may feel that we are not subject to this type of compulsive thought but we are all familiar with activities such as biting our nails or wriggling a foot. There are also the endless compulsory reruns experienced by those who have been through the powerful emotions of separation and loss.)

The effect may be compared to that which results when a computer has received an error in programming that leads to an invalid repetition instruction. This gives rise to an infinite loop which, paying perfect attention to itself, blindly refers back to and responds to an inappropriate command. Like the image in two facing mirrors, consciousness has become locked into itself.

In order to keep track of itself, our brain needs to know what it is doing and it is feedback which tells it this. The question is whether the feedback is coming from the inner world, in which case we may be locked into a loop, or is from outside, encouraging us to explore and measure ourselves against the external world.

A sense of self

How can we know what being caught up in the inner world of another person is like? To begin with, we know that being locked into an inner world is not exclusive to people with learning disabilities. Many of us know about daydreams and how we can become swallowed up in fantasies. The following history explores the experience of a child who had no impairment, to see if we can get a closer idea of what it is that can seduce and trap us into an inner world with its personal fixations.

BIDDY was five when a woman came to look after her while her mother was unable do this. Her previous job had ended when Rose, the child she had been looking after, became ill and died. In her grief, the woman talked incessantly about Rose. Biddy, now adult, looks back and describes what happened:

'One day it dawned on me that it would be much better for me (I should be the object of her love) if I was Rose since it was Rose that my carer was evidently attached to. Somehow I felt myself merging to the point of becoming her – there was a definite sense of movement from 'being me' into 'being Rose'. Thereafter, I refused to respond to any name but hers. This period lasted for about six months and I remember my sadness on leaving her when my Mum was finally able to get through to me. I forgot all this until, as an adult, I found a letter to my mother copied by me and signed, 'Rose'. Enquiring who it was, my sister explained to me. I felt a small flicker of shame at having my inner life so exposed.'

Biddy's search for security led her away from reality and into a closed world which prevented real growth in relation to the world outside. It wasn't until she was able to relinquish her introjection (the unconscious adoption of another person's ideas) that she was able to continue growth and development. However, we have to acknowledge the strength of the feelings that led her into this trap. This was not a conscious decision, it just 'came about' as a response to her need.

Even now I find it difficult to write about Biddy, for she was myself. This is how I know what she felt. I have introduced this personal history because it brings home to me how it is possible, not just to have fantasies, but actually to deal with the bewildering idea that my boundaries might melt so that I, who feel myself to be myself, might 'be' other. In this condition, my centre feels itself to operate from that other place. It is one thing to read about introjection and projection and another to experience the movements and feel their power – processes which we discover in retrospect and then only if we are lucky.

We know others through ourselves – the capacity to dwell on our own relevant experience, however painful, can help us when we come across people caught in similar or analogous situations. Pertinent exploration helps us to make connections, so that behaviour which might otherwise separate us is actually a bond. Their experience is no longer foreign to us. We 'know' from personal experience that when an outer life-situation becomes unbearable, our inner lives can construct an escape route – a fantasy. But we also know that this shift is into a cul-de-sac which does nothing to address our circumstances. While we are in this dead-end, we cannot grow through our difficulties, whatever they are. Empathy takes us to understanding where rationalisation may not be able to reach.

You Don't Know What It's Like

(At the same time we must stand back and think about our insights: we have to learn to dovetail empathy and cognitive processes.)

In the following examples, I am able to recognise when a person's sense of themselves is displaced:

> JOHN's sense of self seems to be located in his foot, JO's in her left shoulder. It is not just that they find these supremely interesting but, working with them, I get the feeling that that they seem to operate from these parts of themselves. This is where they are centred. In both cases, paying attention to the relevant area and using a physical mode of approach (massaging John's foot and applying gentle but firm pressure to Jo's shoulder), enables them to move gradually back to a more normal centre.

The world that Donna Williams, who has ASD, describes as her 'inner world' is by no means totally unconscious, even though she is describing it through retrospective spectacles. She describes it as a retreat from an outer world whose demands were intolerable, given that the world took no account of her particular sensory experience of it. This clash between impossible expectations, which failed to understand her disorientated perception, and her own struggle to make sense of her environment led to withdrawal into a world that seemed safe. In order to survive, she returned to her inner sanctuary. However, this is not the same place as the inner undifferentiated world of the infant. It has its own problems:

> *'Everything in the world is torn up and made redundant – all the relationships one might have had are made with shadows'.*[7]

The question that the autistic brain has to answer is how to retain differentiation in a world that has shut off connection with the 'real world' outside – how to avoid slipping back into unconsciousness. For me, part of an answer is given by a child who, when asked by her doctor why she banged her head, replied that she did it 'to know she was there'.

The child was maintaining her status as a person through physical sensation. If stereotypic behaviour can be said to have a positive function, retaining meaningful contact with consciousness must be one of them: 'While I do this, I know who I am as what I am doing.' Feedback in the form of recognisable sensation from the body to the brain connects me with myself. In a related sense, it is also a defence against anxiety, the anxiety of being overwhelmed by chaos. By focusing on repetitive behaviours, people cut out the sensations which threaten to overload them. When a person is trapped in a loop of stereotypic behaviour, it is not that they are unconscious: the location of the dialogue has shifted from contact with the outer world to their inner world (see **Diagram 1** overleaf).

Even if the stereotypic behaviour relates to something from the outside world, the fixation has, in a sense, hijacked the object and is using it as part of the conversation in the inner world. In this place, the individual is paying total attention to the instructions from the brain saying, for example, over and over again, 'scratch, scratch'. They 'become' this particular feeling in a way that excludes the will to reach out to alternatives. See **Diagram 1** below.

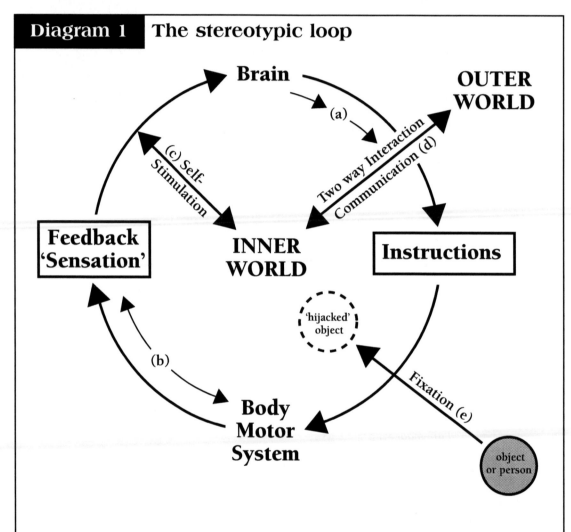

Diagram 1 **The stereotypic loop**

(a)   The brain feeds instructions to the body motor system telling it what to do

(b)   The body responds, giving feedback to the brain in the form of sensation (sound, movement, etc) which triggers another round of the stereotypic loop. The brain and the body are having a conversation with each other. There is no connection with the world outside

(c+d)   Instead of self-stimulation within the inner world (c) we are trying to establish two-way communication with the world outside (d)

(e)   In the case of fixations the inner world hijacks an object or person from the outer world and 'uses' them as part of the furniture of the inner world of stereotypic repetitive behaviour. There is no tone interest in the world outside

When we are trying to gain access to the inner world of a person, we may have to relinquish our own talents and approaches. The reason for this is that an individual may have learned to 'bang a drum' or 'do a jigsaw' in a way that misleads us into thinking that the activity has meaning for them. In fact, they may be doing it in a way that is entirely mechanistic. (This is certainly true of many autistic children who have enormous facility with puzzles but are totally uninterested in the picture or its relation to the real world.) Such facility does nothing to bridge the gap between our world and theirs. It is only when we come empty-handed to a person that we are in a position to enter their inner world, reach them and be with them in a way that gives them confidence and helps them to begin to move out through us. However, this is not the same as feeling we 'become' the person we are working with, in which case we would be no more than a hijacked object. We need to be present in ourselves so they may use us as a bridge to the world outside. They need to be aware of us as an individual as well as our being a vehicle of their language. They need someone to interact with.

Summary

A useful model is to think in terms of the inner and outer world:

- we may not grow fully from the inner to the outer world

- we may retreat back into our inner world

- reflecting on our personal experience may help us enter and respect the inner worlds of other people

- in order to enter private worlds, we may need to relinquish our own agenda.

'THE LADY WITH THE KNIFE'
Resonant Imaging

In this section I want to consider an approach I call 'resonant imaging'. By this, I mean putting oneself empathetically alongside an individual and deliberately using one's own experience as a starting point to generate images which resonate with and give meaning to their lives.

For example, starting with a feeling of my own, I might ask myself: 'What happens if this feeling takes over – how does it feel? Does this present any pictures or images that might be helpful to the person with whom I am working?' (Experience suggests that what resonates for one person may also be resonant for another.) This lateral thinking approach, which allows the mind to drift and throw up related suggestions, requires intuition, flexibility and the ability to discern if an image is helpful or not – since not all will be relevant. Where images and ideas arrived at in this way are seen to 'speak to the person', the outcome can be extremely empowering, establishing creative links and growth where more conventional approaches have been unsuccessful – as the following history illustrates.

MARY is a young woman who lives in a community home. She is able, not autistic. She is extremely volatile, frequently having outbursts when she attacks anything she is near – cars, people, and so on. In discussion with her team leader, it emerges that she has a very poor image of herself and she most often becomes disturbed when she feels 'put down'.

This led me to reflect in personal terms on the fragility of poor self-esteem and how, under these circumstances, anything which I perceive as diminishing may threaten to overwhelm me. I see it as life-threatening and my threshold for extinction is very low. I get trapped in an instinctive response over which I have no control. Trying to stop me reinforces the terror I am experiencing in my inner world and drives me on. I am fighting for my existence.

The team leader and I talked about instinctive responses in terms of how we get locked into them, how under certain circumstances we may still find ourselves prisoners of our biological past when we lived in caves and needed to be able to defend ourselves physically. Groping for ideas, we moved from this image to the possibility of combining it with something like a yellow-card system, introducing visual surprise to try and capture Mary's attention when she was upset. The team leader decided to talk to her about the old times when people used to live in caves and how, in those early days, men and women would have needed to be able to fight and defend themselves against enemies and wild animals. She pointed out that when situations become threatening nowadays, we do not need to prepare to do battle for our lives as we can talk about it. She asked Mary if it would be a good idea to have a picture of a cave woman to hold up when she or her support staff felt that things were getting too much.

Mary understood very well and at this point something astonishing took place – she became conscious of the implications of her behaviour and took on the responsibility for herself. She said, 'No, not a cave woman' and went to her room and brought back a picture of a beautiful woman carrying a knife. Since she knew what she was fetching and exactly where it was, it had obviously struck her as significant when she first saw it, as she had kept it. It already had meaning for her which resonated with the behaviour that she and her team leader were discussing.

With her agreement, her picture was enlarged and laminated. On the back was written in large letters, STOP, THINK, TALK. All staff and Mary had access to it and Mary kept control by ensuring that all new staff were provided with a copy. They held it up to attract her attention when she started to become disturbed. In the following three months, the incidence of Mary's outbursts fell dramatically from several times a week to two episodes during the whole period, which occurred when bank staff were on duty. It was possible to talk her through these using the image.

The degree to which Mary understood the process was illustrated when she saw a fight on TV and said to her team leader that maybe the people involved needed a card system. (She seemed to be unaware of its origins in football.) What she did understand was that people who were caught up in disturbed behaviour could be helped by visual intervention, as she had been.

I have already mentioned a number of situations where an individual may feel themselves to be under life-threat. We know that, under similar apprehensions, we react instinctively.

At a biological level, the most fundamental of all our tasks is self-preservation – whether we like it or not, we are dedicated to preserving our identity, existence and the package we have been issued with known as the selfish genes. **But, in our different realities, we may have completely different thresholds of what constitutes a life-threatening situation.** If our sensory perception of the world starts to disintegrate, or if our feeling of wellbeing in ourselves is minimal, we will feel ourselves under attack very easily and will do battle to preserve ourselves at all cost.

We need to look at how we can help people towards alternative ways of responding – to direct the brain away from trigger-happy reactions towards stability.

Creating new pathways

One possibility is to use the techniques of behaviour modification. This approach is extensively discussed by Lovett. It aims to train people that if they respond in a certain way the consequences will be costly, or there will be a pleasant outcome to 'good' behaviour. Unfortunately, this approach sends a very dubious message to the inner self, that is: 'I'll love you if you are good, I will not love you if you are bad, therefore you are not worth loving for yourself.' This is not the message we are trying to get over to someone with a poor self-image. Interaction should never be tied to a reward scheme. It will increase a person's feeling of impoverishment and undermine self-esteem.[23]

When we are working with such difficulties, we need to undertake a creative search for what one might call 'trip-mechanisms' which will interrupt the dead-end loop in which a person is trapped and open it up, bringing what they are doing within reach of cognitive processes at whatever level. As already suggested, surprise, presented in a respectful way and in the related context of a person's own behaviour is non-threatening and, as such, is often successful. In Mary's case, it involved finding the right image which chimed in with what she already in one sense knew – that is, it was already present in her brain. We just needed the right link. (In neurobiological terms, we needed to establish better neural pathways between the thinking and the emotional emergency response parts of the brain.) We had to find an approach that established a link between inner personal and public outer worlds so that Mary could see that she was not in danger and take charge – take on the responsibility for what was going on for her in her life.

The more we can give people a sense of competence and control, the more likely we are to reduce their feeling of vulnerability which keeps their inner and outer worlds separate. In this quest, a direct approach is most often counter-productive. When they are upset I cannot appeal to their rational mind since links with it are being actively suppressed by the action of adrenaline. Such appeals may threaten the person's unconscious defence systems during confrontation. All I can do is try to understand what is their reality and speak to it in such a way that it grabs their attention. We need to look at the factors in the intervention with Mary which were helpful to her.

- The intervention was based on the premise that because Mary had such a bad image of herself, she was easily thrown into the need to defend her existence if she felt slighted

- When the team leader, a person she trusted, discussed this with her using visual images and language she understood, it clearly 'rang a bell' – to the extent that she recognised the implications and underlying feeling at once. She was able to link these with an alternative representation of difficulties that she had already noted. You could say that at this stage she took it on board, it all 'came together'

- The next stage was for Mary and the team leader to set up what might be called a 'game' with rules – when she was becoming upset, she or staff could hold up a card. It is worth pointing out that the mere existence of the game, with rules that Mary had contributed to, provided a support and safety net, so that her behaviour improved without the need to use it frequently. Her underlying problems were now in the conscious domain – we may surmise that pathways had been set up which gave improved access from the thinking part of her brain to the place where her instinctive responses originated

The key factors which gave Mary's inner feelings a chance to speak were:

- understanding the particular problem she was having

- finding a visual image which addressed her underlying difficulties in a significant and non-threatening way.

Furthermore, Mary's contribution was being valued and she was taking control of her own life in a meaningful way.

I should like to end this section by referring to **Bill**, whose story appears in *Person to Person*. He also attacked people, although not for the same reason as Mary. When he was asked why, Bill would shake his head and say, 'I don't know, I don't know', and it was obvious that he did not. For months we played a game which was especially designed to help him accept the parts of himself that he felt were *so* bad that he could not accept them. It was called 'Goodies and Baddies' and was based on the premise that we all have good and bad parts in ourselves. It did not approach this subject directly but did aim to make it easy to talk in a light-hearted way about awkward situations we could all get into. One day he said:

'You know, I'm not going to get better, am I, while I feel so angry.'

He was as surprised as I was. After this, his outbursts decreased.

You Don't Know What It's Like

Resonant imaging has been used to help people with ASD and those whose behavioural difficulties stem from other sources. In *Person to Person*, the history of **Luke** illustrates the feeling of being contained safely by squares – in his case, patio titles. Luke never trod on the lines. I put myself back in the feeling of being a child playing 'Lines and Squares' and from that designed a game based on flipping a circular piece onto a board marked in squares – aiming to land in a square where it would be safe. It spoke to him at an emotional level and, for the first time, he sat down and joined in.

Culshaw and Purvis stress the need to develop a person's feelings of self-worth and self-esteem.[24] This is not always very easy since the factors underlying a person's low self-image may be extremely deeply embedded. One possibility is to use images with the person that resonate in their individual consciousness in order to try to set up situations where the person feels sufficiently secure to talk about the unspeakable things, the things that they may not even be able to acknowledge to themselves. There is some evidence that simply involving people in helping to identify and manage their own behaviours may assist them, even if they do not fully understand the management strategy (see **Section 12**).

To refer back to the question asked in the **Introduction** as to whether or not we should be training people for responsibility, it is difficult for any of us to take responsibility for our conduct unless we address the difficulties that lie behind it. We can be trained to follow a set of rules but, as pointed out above, this does not motivate us or help us to feel better about ourselves.

Summary

This section reminded us that:

- people with poor self-image may have a very low threshold for triggering the fight-flight response to what is wrongly seen as a life-threatening situation

- we need to give people a sense of competence to reduce the vulnerability which separates their two worlds

- we may be able to help by finding an image which addresses the emotional content of their inner world

- the image may be contained in a 'game' with clearly defined rules

- there is a difference between 'training' a person to take responsibility, which is unlikely to add to their feelings of self-worth, and helping to motivate a person – which does.

Section 9

'MAY I COME IN?'
The idea of control

The idea that we 'need' to control people is insidious and deep-seated. It raises itself in ways we can overlook. For example, the word 'carers' puts us in a dominant position. Substitute the word 'assistant' or 'companion' and we immediately think of ourselves in a different way.

Recently, I was talking about the use of gesture and how we can use this to alert people to what we intend to do, giving them control over whether or not we do it. For example, **Bob** has severe ASD and finds people very difficult. I said that before I entered a room that Bob was in, I paused at the door, pointed to myself and then to the room, and said, 'May I come in?' I was asked if I would have accepted it if Bob had said, 'No.' Would I have gone away? I answered that I would.

Letting a person know that they could control me was more important than my entering the room. Their agenda was more important than mine.

So, what is happening here? I want to go into the room so that I can observe Bob, see what he does and how support staff interact with him. This is my agenda. However, if I am focused on this, I miss the fact that Bob has a different one and that his interaction with me starts when he sees a stranger at the door.

I need to think about Bob's perception of me. In his fragmented world, I may appear not as some*one* but as some*thing* or even as bits of things. He may not know which bits he sees are me and which are him – they float about and the more he tries to focus on them, the more they slip away. Furthermore, as discussed in **Section 4**, apart from the physical perceptual difficulties of processing, Bob's brain may have learned that people are emotionally overloading and be taking steps to avoid this. Bob may not even connect with me at all. Whichever is the case, **I need to reduce my potential as a threat so that Bob can learn that it is safe to connect with me**.

The problem here is that, as carers, we sometimes have a built-in fear about letting the people we work with take control. The question I was asked assumes that this was what the interaction is about. But the interaction is not about who is boss, who is who in the pecking order. What Bob needs to know is that, in his kaleidoscopic world, there is something or someone he can connect with which will not cause him pain. He is engaged in a survival struggle. In order to make that connection, he has to understand that what he does or says will effect change in me, that he is part of a world over which he can, to some extent exert control. This will make him feel safer. It is like being thrown a life-belt.[6]

If I had really needed to come into the room, I might have come back a bit later and asked again. Now that Bob knew he could control me, it would have been safer to let me in. He could predict that I would be sensitive to his difficulties.

I followed this tactic with another person, **Josh**, when playing a game designed around the idea that Josh found squares 'safe'. Letting him control whether or not I made a move by saying 'Yes' or 'No', moved him swiftly from the position of being unable to interact, to sitting up and participating.[1]

It may be more important to let the person have control than to carry out our own agenda.

Summary

We need to:

- think of ourselves as assistants rather than carers; this shifts control to the person we are working with

- respect the individual's agenda.

Section 10

'INTIMATE ATTENTION'
The empowering force of
Intensive Interaction

Most people want to communicate. It is part of the condition of being human.

There are relatively few people who do not respond to an approach in their own language, and Intensive Interaction (echoing back to them a person's own behaviour) is now a well established technique for getting in touch with people who are hard to make contact with otherwise.[25, 26, 27, 28, 29] This is illustrated in the following two histories which relate to two very different disabilities.

> JENNY has very severe learning disabilities and sight impairment. She spends her day in her wheelchair with her head down. She screams when she is unhappy. Support staff at her Resource Centre say that they are unable to make contact with her. She makes a little but quite regular noise, sucking her saliva. When I listen to this and echo it back, she pays attention and starts to smile. She sucks hers in a definite rhythm and waits to see if I will copy this. We alternate her sounds. She puts her head up and laughs out loud. Three members of her support team try this with her and she enjoys the interactions for over an hour.

Moving to the second history, Janice has very severe ASD.

JANICE is in her mid thirties. She has become very withdrawn since the death of members of her family. When she comes to the centre, she gets stuck at the gate, looking out between the slats of the fence. Efforts to persuade her to come in can last for over an hour. When she does come in, she stands by the glass door and looks out. She stays there all day. It is difficult to persuade her to move into the dining area for a meal. She stands on the threshold of the dining room rocking backwards and forwards. By the time she is ready to move in, her dinner is cold and has to be taken away to be re-heated. When Janice sees it disappear she concludes that dinner is over and returns to her post by the door. The whole process has to start again.

Surprise presented in the context of an individual's own language is one of the key elements which enables a person to shift from their inner world to the world outside. Starting at the gate, her keyworker and I used this as a technique: Janice's keyworker went outside and looked back at Janice through the slats of the fence. This immediately shifted her attention from her inner world to an intriguing situation which had arisen in the world outside – something that falls within the 'looking through the slats' behaviour (which is part of her experience) is now different. She starts to smile and when her keyworker comes back through the gate she is able to take advantage of Janice's attention. Janice immediately takes her arm and comes inside.

Once inside Janice takes up her customary position by the door. Her body language is, as usual, completely negative, arms folded tightly across her chest, looking out of the door. Occasionally she rubs her chin on her shoulder.

Her keyworker points out that behind her folded arms she is constantly engaged in rubbing her fingers. This is the way she talks to herself. We start to do the same, showing her what we are doing. This captures her attention, she likes it and smiles. I move into making a game of touching thumbs. She unfolds her arms and reaches out to do it more easily. Eventually I ask if I may rub her shoulders, as she does to herself when she rubs it with her chin. We move into sharing this form of interaction. She pushes her shoulder forwards for me to rub. By now we are interacting easily with each other. After about an hour I have to move on but during the rest of the morning, whenever I pass her, we touch thumbs. It has become our way of saying 'hi' to each other.

Looking at the problem of how to manage dinner, we decide that her body language is telling us that the room is too noisy and full of people for her to come in. We wait until the others have finished and moved out before inviting her to come and eat. Her keyworker brings the plate to her where she stands by the door and offers her a mouthful. However she still will not come in until I ask her if either the little soft dog she clutches or her thumbs would like some dinner. (This is an indirect approach through her acceptable point of contact and in therefore non-threatening). She nods and comes at once, sits down and eats her dinner. When she has finished she asks for a cup of tea. She then asks to go to the toilet – something she has not done before. Staff continue to use her language with her and three weeks later she was still in contact. They know how to talk to her and she is responding. (At this point it is crucial to remember that if we develop a successful strategy with people with ASD we must not remove it when they improve. We have not 'cured' the ASD – only modified their environment.)

Why does Intensive Interaction work so well? What is it about it that makes us feel good, that helps us to feel confident? Why is it so empowering? One of the objections sometimes raised when I am teaching is that: *'It's too easy, it can't make that much difference.'*

In essence, to reflect a person's behaviour back to them is a very simple idea, yet time and again it *does* make a difference. Sometimes that difference appears very quickly. A person who we would say is completely 'switched off' comes to life almost immediately, and those who have been indifferent to their surroundings become alert and attentive. After he had been watching a session of Intensive Interaction, a support worker – who had been finding it very difficult to make contact with a man who was very withdrawn – said: *'Today I saw the real person.'*

So why does it work – and what do we mean by 'the real person'? What are we tapping into that makes it so effective a bridge between a person's inner world and the world outside, the world of 'me' and 'not me', so that a person begins to find the confidence to move from solitary self-stimulation to shared activity?

A depth of mutual attention

Deep down, we all feel vulnerable. We live behind some sort of mask, hoping it will shield our lurking vulnerabilities from the world.

But suppose I have very severe learning disabilities or ASD or both? If the world I live in is confusing and fragmented and I am not sure which bits of it are 'me' and which 'not me', the only place where I have a sense of my own identity is in my personal inner world. I cannot connect to the world outside. If I engage in stereotypic repetitive behaviour, these signals are hard-wired in, they do not break up. In this way, I can talk to myself and know who I am. It is only by using the repetitive behaviours of my stereotype that you can talk to me without threatening my sense of identity. This ties up with observations that individuals may be capable of understanding more complex speech than normal when one is working within the stereotype. Increased confidence puts less stress on the processing system so it operates more efficiently.

Ephraim suggests that the processes involved in Intensive Interaction are the same as those in the infant learning pattern where the parent figure confirms the infant's sounds and signals.[30] At the same time as the infant brain recognises the confirmatory response, it is also surprised that this did not come from itself and begins to look outside itself for the source. (I have witnessed this surprise on the face of a woman who realised I was echoing back her self-injurious behaviour. Her jaw literally dropped as she took in that I was tapping my cheek every time she hit herself.)

As pointed out in the history of Janice, surprise is a very important element in the process. If we think of the model of trying to open the door of a locked room, surprise is both the hand that opens it and the foot in the door that keeps it ajar – it allows the process of interaction to flow.

When we were working together, a speech therapist said, 'I have worked for many years on a one-to-one basis but I have never experienced such intimate attention as I do when I see or use Intensive Interaction.' I was intrigued by the phrase, 'intimate attention', not really having thought through the physical bonding that is the common denominator of this type of intervention.

When I work, I am having a conversation with someone, a conversation without words. We are wholly present for each other, nothing else exists. All our attention, everything we are, is focused in the other person. That sensory sensation is overtaken by a feeling of total mutual trust to the extent of shared experience – we become lost in each other. We examine each other with minute attention, giving weight and value to every movement, sound and sensation. All sense of self is transferred to the activated part. Although both participants are 'present' it also feels as though they have 'become' the sensory area of interaction. Links are formed which bypass the cognitive processes. We shall never feel quite the same about each other as before the intervention.

Intensive Interaction addresses the emotional state of a person. For both of us, it is a creative opportunity where we can let each other know how we feel – and also test each other out using the simplicity of body language, without the complications of misunderstanding which are the downside of using words.

It is important to realise that this experience of total awareness of other/self has nothing to do with like or dislike. It is totally non-judgemental. The intellect is not involved – it is pure sensation.

This sensation feels good, it is very empowering and often extends beyond the time of interaction. Apart from enjoying themselves, participants usually become relaxed. A person's compulsive behaviour may slow or stop while they appear to drift in the experience.

You Don't Know What It's Like

It is important to emphasise that this dynamic is not dependent on the type of intervention; that is, it is not just the outcome of touch, of movement or of sound, or of sharing some particular fixation. Rather, it is the depth of mutual attention through which we let each other know that we have understood each other – that we can talk to each other and delight in doing so – that is so powerful.

A 'first friend'

I want to compare this experience with one which is common to all of us – how we behave when we move into a new situation. Although we appear to be social animals, we live with the paradox that when we first move into a group of people who are new to us, we do not immediately identify with the group. Instead, we weigh up the individuals, looking for a potential friend. This friend will be our ally in what, however much we want to be part of the group, is potentially a battleground because it is unpredictable. We do not know our way around and it is easy to get things wrong and upset people. Our success in the group depends on our finding someone who, as we say, 'speaks our language', so that they can 'show us the ropes'.

What I am suggesting is that, in order to be able to move more freely from their inner personal life to the new situation of taking part in a public outer world, non-verbal people also need a 'first friend' who will act as their ally and bridge. By learning a person's language, we can act as that first friend so that, gaining confidence through us, they can begin to look at the world outside.

Returning to Jenny, described at the beginning of this section, after three weeks of intervention using her sounds, she now sits with her head up more frequently. Staff say that she is both calmer and more alert. Now that they know how to talk to her, they feel confident working with her. Now that she is able to get a response, she is finding it worthwhile to hold up her head and look at what is happening round her.

A month after the intervention with Janice and continued use of her language by staff, they reported that she was still making progress – 'it seems like a breakthrough'. They now know how to talk to her and she is responding.

Summary

Using Intensive Interaction can be a powerful way of establishing communication.

- Using a person's inner language enables us to communicate with them directly in a way that they understand and which is non-stressful

- The respectful use of surprise within the context of the language helps the interaction to flow

- Mutual attention is crucial

- Our role is to act as a 'bridge' from a person's inner world to the outer world, and also as the 'first friend' who helps them to cross over

Section 11

'SPEECH MAY BE SOUND WITHOUT MEANING'
Communication and comprehension

In his book on management thinking, DeBono points out that communication requires both parties to have similar languages of perception:

> 'If the receiver's language is known to be totally different, the communicator must know how to switch into that language. This obviously applies when the word language is used in its direct sense but it equally applies when it is used symbolically for perceptions and values.' [31]

In other words, it may not only be that the person we are trying to communicate with does not understand us, but that they see the world in a different way. He continues:

> 'Too often we try to teach the other person our language and concepts and then communicate with them in this language. We do this because we fear that [their] language may not contain the sophisticated concepts we need in the communication.'

He concludes that we should always communicate in the other person's language.

This also applies to our attempts to communicate with people who are non-verbal. They almost certainly do see the world differently and the language they use to talk to themselves is one we do not recognise as having meaning. So often we talk about communication as though it were a simple process of exchanging information. While this is true, it is only part of a much more complex and subtle process which involves social assessment and reassurance: I need to know where I stand and who will support me, be my own ally. Apart from letting each other know what we want, communication is a delicate probing of feelings using facial and body language in the hope that you will feel good about me so that I can feel good about myself. It is about security, both internal and external, and is essential to our wellbeing.

When we are working with people who are difficult to reach, we usually focus exclusively on trying to get them to understand what we want and giving them ways of letting us know what they want – an exchange of basic needs. Yet even here, we frequently present information in ways that people do not understand. As Peeters points out in his book *Autism*, the most essential aspect of any attempt at communication is that it is presented in the way that is most likely to be understood – people must be able to take on board what we are offering. This applies both to our attempts to communicate with people through their inner personal language and also how we try to inform them. **We need to use the system which is most likely to be effective for that individual.**[32]

It is no use, for example, using signs with a person who is unable to cope with abstract concepts and who thus cannot attach meaning to them. Yet, knowing this, we sometimes spend years trying to get people to use systems which will always be incomprehensible to them. They may eventually make a sign for 'please' and 'thank you' but still not under-stand what they are doing. It is just a motion they have to go through, for example, before they get their tea. (Incidentally, in the context of age-appropriateness, insisting that someone say please and thank you is something we do to children, not to adults.)

This is not to undervalue systems of signing which can be liberating when used appropri-ately; it is their blanket misuse in inappropriate situations which can be counterproductive. We sometimes have to suspend our attachment to specific strategies and look realistically at the cognitive difficulties people face which may make it impossible to use a particular way of getting in touch. In such situations we need to explore alternatives and those alternatives are wide-ranging. We need to look at the whole repertoire of a person's body and facial language, how they move, and the sounds they make. Even if the language consists of incidental grunts, or clicks which are non-intentional, these may relate to activities which the person enjoys. (For example, as described in *Person to Person*, the clicks made by Hannah when eating food she enjoyed, were used to distract her when she was afraid.)

We must also take note of anything external to the person in which they show positive interest, such as tearing paper, or the wind blowing in their face. Surprisingly, we often find that an individual's personal language offers us a wealth of ways to express and enrich feeling. There is also the downside – sensory stimuli which cause a person stress and trigger off negative responses. These also are part of the person's language – in metaphorical terms, the 'bad words' which may disturb them so much that their world breaks apart. The person feels under attack and responds accordingly.

> **LIZA cannot bear the word 'pull' and attacks people when she hears it.**

We can only speculate as to the origin of Liza's distress but it is real enough. She behaves as though she needs to tear the world apart, it is so bad.

Finding the right language

On the practical level, if we are going to communicate, first of all we need to attract a person's attention; in getting this, we need to be sure they have no physical impairment. In spite of improvements in services, it is surprisingly common to encounter adults with severe learning disabilities whose deafness is undiagnosed, or whose hearing has not been tested recently. Particularly, deafness in one ear is often unrecognised. A person cannot respond to voice if they do not hear it.

> **THOMAS stands by the door at the centre all day, watching everything intently with a slightly puzzled look on his face. He is wearing a T-shirt printed with a steamship. I tell him I have sailed on it. Since he does not respond, I make the deep sound of its siren. Immediately, his face clears. I have made a low-frequency sound he can hear. He follows me about hopefully for the next two days, waiting for that precious sound.**

We also need to present our communication in a way that a person can handle. People with severe learning disabilities who have little or no sight frequently curl up and cut off from the world completely. Their experience of the world may have been hazardous, particularly if they have been in large institutions. 'Touch' has been bad news. They do not want us near them. At the same time, they are desperately in need of input to replace their visual loss (which is about three-quarters of their total sensory uptake).

Such people usually provide themselves with a substitute language; this may take a number of forms, such as rocking or rubbing their own fingers. Since they cannot see and very often dislike touch, it is difficult to reflect these movements back to them, to speak to them in their own language. But it is possible, for example, to reflect rocking back to a person by banging your feet on the floor in time with their rocking movements so that they feel the vibration, or to scratch the material of a person's chair in time with their finger movements. If a person is also deaf, we may be able to reach them by sitting on the far end of the sofa and bouncing to their rocking rhythm. This type of intervention is frequently successful, shifting a person's interest from self-stimulation to the unexpected source of the echo. People uncurl, lift their heads and start to smile with recognition. Once a person is interested, it becomes easier to interact; they are not in a threatening situation and will begin to be more tolerant of touch, so that movements may be echoed more directly – on a person's back, for example.

If all is well on the sensory front, we still need to be sure that a person is really attending before we try to communicate. We have to look at their language, how they talk to themselves. We need to use this, sometimes in an exaggerated way, to hold their interest.

Picking out exactly what a person will respond to can sometimes be complicated, as is illustrated in the next two histories.

> **VAL**, who is very withdrawn, makes humming noises but does not respond to these when they are echoed back by staff. Listening to her carefully suggests that these sounds are in fact part of a cycle of breath holding – inhalation, hum, hold, breath out. Focusing on the explosive exhalation which ends the cycle and copying that sound on the Kazoo does catch her attention. Val starts to sit up and smile and listen, waiting for me to echo her.

> **DON**, who has little speech, tugs at his collar to emphasise things. Sometimes his support staff feel he is just saying, 'This is me, Don.' At other times, he grabs people's collars and won't let go. This behaviour is discouraged as inappropriate and uncomfortable. However, in order to get and hold Don's attention, I make use of his gestures, waggling my own collar in an exaggerated way. He thinks this is extremely funny. Moving from rejecting me, we begin to laugh together and become good friends. It stimulates him to try to engage his peers – pointing from them to me and showing them what I was doing. His good humour spills over and is infectious in the group.

From isolation to integration

It is important to reiterate that in order to get in touch with people who are difficult to reach, we have to learn their language. This is because not all staff are aware of the crucial part that developing relationships plays in communication. It is at least as important, if not more so, as exchanging needs-information. Dunbar points out that letting each other know how we feel about ourselves and each other may have been an important factor in the evolution of language.[2] We can use it to bring affection and security into an imprisoned world.

Some of the questions staff ask about Intensive Interaction are about the mechanics of it – how long and how frequent should sessions be? Because of the way it arose initially, through school periods or therapeutic sessions, we have tended to use limited times. However, in community home settings, more and more staff are saying that they want to use it as a way of communicating whenever it seems natural, just as one might chat to friends. This is precisely what Intensive Interaction gives us the option of doing – it is a way of expressing our enjoyment of being with another, of being at ease together. Mutual trust and confidence start to build and difficult behaviours frequently diminish as the person no longer feels isolated and defensive. There is often a marked change in how staff feel about their work. Everyone is able to take a more relaxed attitude. The group dynamic has improved.

Sometimes staff are concerned as to how this type of interaction will be viewed by the general public. It is possible to argue that some directions suggested in this book are so individually based as to lead away from social acceptance. If we learn a person's language and use it with them, will it not isolate them rather than move them towards integration?

We need to take a hard look at exactly what we have in mind when we talk about 'social integration' for an individual with profound disabilities or very severe autism. These are people who may have completely rejected their environment because they find it confusing, hostile or frightening. Further, our world may have rejected their overtures to us, the only way they have of getting in touch with us.

If we are not careful, our expectations may lead to conformity rather than communication, respectability rather than respect, and valuing a person for what we think they *ought* to be rather than what they *are*.

At a community home for children with profound disability and multiple impairment, it was suggested that communication was not possible and therefore staff focused on reducing inappropriate behaviour so the children would be able to take their place in public. With the best intentions, what was being aimed at was conformity. The effect, however, was somewhat contrary to that intended. Suppression of such behaviour as raspberry noises, for example, seemed to lead, not to compliance but to other forms of 'naughty' behaviour such as grabbing at people or objects – anything to get attention.

By ignoring or erasing a person's own language, we may cut off the one way they are able to interact with us – we seal up their prison.

While not suggesting that socially inappropriate language should be wildly and exaggeratedly used in public, it is quite often possible to develop shorthand reinforcers which maintain contact with a person without attracting unwanted attention. We should ask ourselves if we see a group of people as more 'adult' when half are sitting in dulled conformity while the other half chat amongst themselves, or when all the group are participant and enjoying themselves – when we see people with impairment truly being valued for themselves. To change attitudes, the public needs to see people with impairment who are self-assured and with whom communication is being taken seriously.

One technique used to keep in touch is the 'running commentary', with the aim of letting people know what we are presently doing with them. However, if we watch a video of ourselves doing this, we very often see that we are engaging in a monologue – we are saying things without involving an individual personally; we are thinking about what *we* are doing and not about them. For example, we may be talking to a person about putting their socks on while ignoring the grunts they are making. This does not engage their attention; in other words, our running commentary ignores their signals since it is fixed on what we are doing. It is not meaningful enough to promote response. To communicate, we need to pay attention to who the person really is instead of who and what we want the person to be. We can sometimes help with this by watching the person's face very carefully while we speak and exaggerating facial language to accompany what we say – for example, raising our eyebrows and smiling. (This is not an appropriate technique if a person is avoiding eye contact.)

Finding a point of contact

There is also the problem that what a person is doing very often has no meaning for us. It is so easy to say, 'they are not doing anything'. We may also find a person's language to themselves very off-putting. Excess noise is only irritating when it is not seen as *communication*. Once it is recognised for what it is, it becomes a potential point of access rather than a barrier.

The fact that two people are not really communicating may be because neither is doing anything which has meaning for the other. This was illustrated for me by a woman with autism who was locked into delayed echolalic speech.

JILL gets locked into a particular sing-song phrase which she repeats endlessly. She is very tense. It is not possible to break into the phrase or divert her into some more meaningful speech. Even when I repeat her phrase back to her, she takes no notice. I recall a clip from a video interview of Donna Williams talking about how speech may be sound without meaning. She shows a clip of a child repeating the shape and noise of his teacher's sentence without words. I try this with Jill, just using the pitch and rhythm of her speech but not her echolalic words. She becomes relaxed, leans forward and is deeply engaged in what I am doing. Her echolalia ceases.

I could make no relevant sense of Jill's echolalia and, when I was talking to her, Jill could make no sense of the sounds that came from me – they did not 'speak' to her in a way that engaged her attention. However, when I removed the confusing element of words, she could recognise what she heard and knew that it related to her. She responded with interest. A member of her support staff commented that the interaction between us became very intense in a way that was unusual for Jill.

We may sometimes feel that a person is doing nothing which we can latch on to. However, careful observation reveals this is rarely so – almost everyone pays attention to something, even if it is simply breathing. The techniques of Intensive Interaction give us ways of setting up true communication through the simplest bodily activities.

Summary

- In order to get in touch with a person, we need not only to use their personal language but also to try and understand their perception of the world

- If a person cannot understand abstract concepts, they may not be able to understand signs

- If we ignore a person's language, we may never be able to get in touch with them or they with us

- We may need to look at all the ways a person talks to himself or herself, not just through their repetitive behaviour

Section 12

'YES OR NO?'
Making choices

Helplessness may be learned as well as innate. If we are to have a say in our lives, we need not only to be able to make choices but also to be given the opportunities to do so. Guess[33] presents a spectrum of progressive empowerment, moving from choice as preference (which may be expressed non-verbally in a receptive reactive environment), through choice as decision-making and selection of alternatives, to choice as self-advocacy and taking charge of one's life: 'I need to be able to tell you what I want and I need you to listen to me and act on my request.'

In this section, I focus on choice as preference indication and look at some of the ways in which we may facilitate this. I also want to examine the special situations that may arise when people with autism are unable to process information or organise responses, which may lead them to experience 'choice' as positively disempowering. In such situations, overloading leads to fragmentation and the person can become seriously disturbed.

First of all, it appears that, regardless of whether or not the person has fully understood and is making the correct choice, the very act of being involved in choice may in itself be empowering.

Williams and Jones describe a study where the effect of self-monitoring behaviour on reducing agitated/disruptive behaviour in community group homes was measured. A woman with learning disabilities who was aggressive was asked, after each incident, to tick on a chart whether she had handled or lost her temper. The chart had appropriate faces on it and, she was asked to tick the appropriate column. She co-operated but was not able to evaluate herself correctly. Nevertheless, the number of aggressive incidents dropped by 40%. This suggests that facilitating the participants' engagement in the process of developing verbal rules has a reinforcement potency in itself.[34] As with 'the lady with the knife' (see **Section 8**) the very fact that the woman was involved, and her contribution was valued, increased her feelings of self-worth and elevated the threshold at which she was overtaken by aggression.

Secondly, we may be able to take active steps to facilitate understanding so that the individual is more involved – they *know* what they are saying. In the following history, a woman who is often disturbed appears to be able to make choices.

> JANE nods her head clearly for 'yes' and shakes it for 'no'. At the centre, she shook her head when offered the foot spa but when it was removed she immediately became very upset. It was clear that she did want it but had indicated 'no' when she meant 'yes'. Subsequent observation suggested that she quite often got her answer wrong but she did know that she was being asked a question which required a response, so she said 'yes' or 'no'. As there was a 50% chance of being right, it had been assumed that she was able to indicate preference but in fact she was frequently incorrect. Not getting what she wanted was one of the more frequent triggers of her outbursts.

Swain, reviewing learned helplessness and empowerment through choice, points out that successful working with choice-as-preference is directly dependent on the sensitivity, empathy and responsiveness of support staff.[35] In Jane's case, staff followed a suggestion that after she had indicated 'No', they partially removed the foot spa so that she could see the consequences of what she had said, then gave her a second chance by looking at her enquiringly to see how she responded. This enabled Jane to make an informed choice and the outbursts that had been related to misunderstanding diminished.

Negotiating choices

The skill of negotiation demands that we observe what causes a problem for a particular individual and work out ways of meeting the difficulty. As a colleague observed, we need to think about what we are doing all the time. We think we do this, but very often we are thinking about how the situation affects us and not about the difficulties which the individual concerned is struggling with. We need to put aside what we see – in this case, distressed and disturbed behaviour which is difficult to handle – and, having observed what the source of the problem is, look for creative ways of resolving it. We need to look for the underpinning causes of challenging behaviour rather than working directly with it.

In order to negotiate successfully, we need to be sure that: firstly, we have a person's attention; secondly, that we present information or choices in a way that they understand

and find non-threatening. The latter particularly applies to people with autism who may find direct communication far too confrontational and demanding to handle. Only if we find a 'safe' way of offering information will they be able to process it. Because of the danger of overload if our approach is not understood, once we have got their attention, we may need to accompany our speech with secondary clues. The mode we employ will depend on an individual's level of understanding. It may be that the person can cope with pictures. For example, the PECS system – where a child has to take pictures Velcroed into a book and hand them to their teacher/parent (who says the word at the same time as receiving the picture) – helps the child to associate words with interaction; it puts meaning into the verbal exchange. Preliminary work suggests that this system can be very effective with pre-school children. Not only does it help them to understand that exchange is involved in communication, but they also learn to initiate contact. A greater proportion have been developing speech than could have been forecast. Some work has been done with adults and, although they have not developed speech, their ability to communicate is improved.[36]

Simple gestures and perhaps objects of reference that a person can feel also help. Quite often a person with autism will start to do something and then get stuck (their motor system becomes disconnected from their brain) and they stand waiting. The person can become very stressed at this point, torn between an expectation that they will do something and an inability to perform. They need a 'clue' to reconnect. Even people who are quite able can benefit from gestures and objects of reference, especially if they find it difficult to look at pictures. (Even if the person is high-functioning they may, in order to process at least some of the incoming signals, have switched off hearing or seeing. Offering a signal to an alternative sense may get through to them so that they know what we are going to do.)

Jolliffe says that she found things so much easier to understand through touch and feeling[9] and Williams also describes how she developed sensing through feeling.[7]

If we have managed to help a person understand, we need to look for signs of agreement such as a quick nod of the head. Agreement means the person is participating in what happens in their lives instead of being dragged along by events.

> I am working with BEN, whose sensory world is chaotic. With him, I might say, 'May I sit down?' accompanied by a gesture pointing to a chair. I look for acknowledgement by a flicker of the eyes. Ben knows where I am, what I am going to do and has agreed to my doing it. I know that he has processed and understood my request, and is not likely to find an unanticipated action so intimidating that he will attack me.

If we are going to give choices, we need to be sure that the person understands them or we may add to their difficulties. There may be circumstances where the effect of choice is just too overwhelming and in spite of what we believe to be a beneficial and respectful approach, we may need to avoid it altogether. This possibility is explored in the next history.

DEBBIE is six and at school. She has autism and is unable to join class activities except when they involve food. She can tolerate sitting in a group when there is a biscuit or orange juice in sight. (If we are right about certain activities being 'hard-wired' into the brain, in her disordered world, when she is eating, she knows what she is doing. Otherwise there is chaos.) At other times, Debbie is extremely upset and disrupts the class trying to look for the biscuit tin or wanders round outside flicking her fingers or some string. Sometimes she stops and looks at her reflection in a dark window. She 'knows' a few Makaton signs but does not use them meaningfully.

Debbie has a special worker who takes her to activities such as the gym or sensory room. In the gym, Debbie will sometimes bounce a ball or jump on the trampoline but she tends to do this in a rather mechanical way.

Her keyworker is careful to offer Debbie choices. She says, 'Go and stand by the door if you want to go to the hall,' but Debbie does not respond to such options. She retreats to her finger movements. Repeated offers simply confuse her and she ends up attacking a nearby person. However, we find that she responds at once if we give her a ball to hold, point to the hall and say, 'Hall'. Every time she is given a clear objective in a way that she understands, she complies immediately.

Debbie is not being difficult. She simply cannot handle the information she needs to process in order to make choices. If we look at it from her point of view, we can see that trying to process alternatives is more stressful than understanding a simple request made in such a way that she can grasp and respond to.

Summary

- Making choices may be empowering but is not always so, particularly for some people with autism
- We must present choices in a way that a particular person can understand
- Sometimes people will need a second chance to see the consequences of their choice
- We need to simplify our language and, where appropriate, confirm it by using gesture and /or objects of reference

Section 13

'COPY AND PASTE'
Transferring a positive emotional load

As we learn any new language, we become more fluent in its use. We learn which elements indicate pleasure, which signify security and when a person is unhappy or becoming disturbed. Whatever the language, we look not only for sounds but for all the facial and body language that expresses feelings. By learning to use the elements that are meaningful to a person, we can enhance our empathetic communication with each other. We let them know we have taken on board their feelings and understand them. We can let them know what our feelings are.

It is sometimes possible to start to bring security where there is fear by moving a sound that has positive associations for a person to situations where they feel insecure. This can be particularly helpful to people within the autistic spectrum who are experiencing overload or fragmentation.

In **Section 4**, we looked at Donna Williams' description of her battle to understand what was going on in her life. Many people with ASD take refuge from the chaos in repetitive or compulsive behaviours. In a slippery world, they set up markers where they know what is going on.

In connection with this I should like to look at the particular fixation which some people develop around 'drinks'.

First of all, we know that some medication makes people extremely thirsty. They really do want an awful lot to drink, much more than fits in with conventional tea-breaks. However, I want to suggest a secondary component to this behaviour. When a person is living in a totally disordered world, certain things are landmarks. As we have explored before, according to Barron, when they are involved in repetitive behaviours, they recognise what they are doing.[10] Momentarily, the fragments in the kaleidoscope settle and they can see the pattern of what is going on – even if it is restricted to their inner world.

> **MIKE, who has very severe autism, spends much of his time outside in the garden. He finds people very difficult and chooses to separate himself from them. At intervals he presents himself at the door and says 'Drinks', with particular emphasis on the 'KS' at the end. It does not seem to mean anything to him to say, 'Soon', or some such time indicator. After he has had two drinks, instead of replying, I try just repeating back to him his sound, 'KS', 'KS'. He is immediately interested and pays attention to me. We get a conversation going between us, alternating his sounds between us. He relaxes and stops asking for drinks. Instead of running away, he comes inside the house. We sit down on the sofa together. I whisper 'KS' in his ear and he likes it.**

What I suggest is that Mike **knew what was happening** when he was drinking. In between drinks, his anxiety rose. This could be allayed by tuning in to a contextual signal, one that he associated with drinks in a way that was also non-threatening. It was a sound he could attend to without fear of fragmentation – of the signals breaking up. Fascination with this new presentation of 'his' sound enabled him to attend to the world outside. Mike's support staff used this as a way of making contact with him on a regular basis, both the sounds on their own and as 'bilingual' clues to draw attention to 'information'; for example, 'KS, KS, Mike, bath'. In this sense, one is 'gift-wrapping' information in the language a person feels secure with.

If we refer back to Sian Barron's account of the security he obtained from his repetitive behaviour (see **Section 3**), we can see that **what we are doing is placing our demand – that Mike have a bath – within the safe haven of a communication system that is Mike's way of letting himself know where he is and what he is doing. This renders it non-stressful and easy for him to process**.

Mike's staff also standardised what they said to him. For example, one of the times in the day Mike found most difficult was when he woke up. (This early morning confusion seems to be characteristic of some people with autism.) All staff woke him in the same way and this helped him through this period.

Mike and his support staff got to know and trust each other. He began to come in and was able to sit with a group briefly. Sometimes he would invite staff to sit with him by patting the sofa. He smiled and laughed in appropriate contexts. Whereas he had always become upset when he had to get out of a car before, he could now do so without hitting out. He was generally much more friendly and staff felt more able to handle things on the rare occasions when he was disturbed.

Mike's home is an assessment centre for seriously disturbed service users, some of whose difficulties make great demands on its dedicated staff. For this reason, staff have had to shift their priorities for the time being. Mike is no longer able to receive the attention he was previously getting and at present his outbursts, which were greatly reduced, have returned. This regression emphasises that if one is able to put into place a structure which helps a person with autism to feel safe, it must be maintained. As I point out in *Person to Person*, the positive outcomes are not the result of 'curing' the autism but of modifying the environment.

Creating a buffer zone

Mike was anxious about having drinks because, although he knew what he was doing when he drank, reality slipped away in between times and he could not gauge when it would return as he had no grasp of interval. We took a roundabout way to reassure him, detaching an element of his speech – 'KS' – which related to the stability he associated with drinking, and moved it, together with its positive emotional load, to anchor him in a situation where he was vulnerable to his anxiety. Putting it in computer language, we are talking about 'copy and paste', where a section of text is copied and moved from one page to another.

Mike is not the only person with whom this 'copy and paste' technique has been used. Hannah, described in *Person to Person*, made inadvertent jaw clicks when she was eating, an activity she enjoyed, and these were used to divert her when she was being lifted, a situation which frightened her.

This positive feedback offered her a way out of her inner world when she was locked into an unhappy state. We may be able to use this strategy to tap into the inner world of a person when they have become locked into escalating stress as in the history of Kev which follows. Here, we are using the rhythm of his self abuse which he recognises.

> **KEV hits himself when upset and becomes increasingly self-abusive. Eventually, he starts to lash out at people near him. Echoing back to him the rhythm of his smacks by knocking the table surprises him and he moves from being absorbed in his internal stress to looking round to see where 'his' sound is coming from. His attention shifts from his locked-in personal world to the world outside. He stops hitting himself and begins to engage with staff.**

When we use a person's personal code to release them from the cycle in which they are trapped, we act as a bridge to the world outside. As with all codes, the key is very specific and, in order for it to work, we may need to use *exactly* the words, sounds or rhythms the person is using – simply putting oneself alongside a person empathetically may not seem to be enough to spring the trap.

ROGER is autistic. He attends a large and, inevitably at times, noisy day centre, almost the last environment that one would think was a suitable background against which to effect improvement.

Roger wanders the day centre in a world of his own. He is disturbed by other service users and hits out at them if they come too near. He has quite frequent serious outbursts and is unable to take part in activities or even to go out on the centre bus.

As with Mike, staff reflected back to Roger his sounds and repetitive behaviours. He became more aware of them and interactive with them. A predictable mini-environment was provided for him by using a team to work with him – they were always people he knew and who worked with him in the same way. This stability was extended to respite care so that he always received the same responses, even when he woke.

The team tried out a number of approaches. Initially, they found Roger so exhausting that they tried working in two-hour shifts. There was no improvement in his behaviour. Reflecting on this, they saw that the constant turnover of staff might be stressful to him (as working with him was for staff). Management used this insight to help staff understand the nature of stress that Roger was experiencing. With management support, the team switched to working with Roger all day and found that the consistency that this provided, combined with other strategies such as Intensive Interaction (not in sessions, but using his sounds with him all the time in combination with verbal language where appropriate) was beneficial. His outbursts started to reduce.

The team studied Roger's behaviour carefully and learned to distinguish between outbursts which were triggered by pain – he had problems with his ears – and those which indicated he was upset and could not cope with the situation in which he found himself. They learned to value and be encouraged by small improvements. They learned how to keep the right distance during outbursts and handle them in a manner that did not escalate his disturbed behaviour.

The use of these combined approaches has made it possible for Roger to begin to relate to people, not only his team but also other service users, in a more friendly way. He clearly does not feel so threatened by them and may smile if they call his name. With his team he can go on the centre bus with another service user. On a good day, he can go out to lunch in a pub.

His mother says that at home Roger's outbursts are greatly diminished and are now usually related to pain, or sometimes unanticipated changes. At the centre, serious recorded disturbances have dropped from fourteen per week to one in six weeks (averaged over six months).

During this period, staff have focused not so much on teaching Roger how to do things but on how to be with him and communicate with him. Roger has always had a few words but has begun to use a wider range in an appropriate way. His latest achievement is to say, 'Coke' to the barman, hand over his money and wait for his change. This is a major step forward for him.

In spite of progress in his ability to relate and make use of appropriate words, the team still use his sounds to keep in touch with Roger. In a world which he still perceives as chaotic, keeping that link open is vital.

For Roger, what was needed to effect positive alteration in his life (which has resulted in improved behaviour) was the introduction by staff of what might be termed a predictable protective shield. This acted as a buffer zone which insulated him from externally generated sensory overload and also internally generated emotional overload. The 'buffer zone' provided a recognisable secure haven in which he could interpret the sensory and emotional input he received, even in the difficult environment where he lived.

Because he was now held together within familiar structure – and language was used in a form which he could process – Roger knew what was going to happen. Staff could keep in touch through his sounds – sounds which were not inappropriate in a public context. All an outsider would witness was an occasional murmured conversation between friends. This progress, which was achieved through the work of committed staff and good leadership, was the outcome of looking deeply at the underlying difficulties Roger was experiencing.

This buffer zone is not the same as a 'womb' which would cut a person off from the external world and, in effect, infantilise them. Rather, the environment is rearranged so that the individual has improved access to the outer world and can enjoy it without fear. Reduction in the quantity of input that is interpreted as 'hostile' results in improved processing and ability to relate to the world. Interestingly, Williams observes that when her visual confusion is reduced through the use of tinted Irlen lenses, her auditory acuity improves – she can understand sound better.[18] It is my experience that when one is working *within* the stereotype, and therefore in a way that presents reduced threat, people with autism can interpret more complex language than is normally possible for them. Further, working in this way allows people to express their feelings and they will frequently do so – through direct eye contact, smiling, laughter and, even if they cannot normally tolerate physical contact, with hugs. People with severe autism may begin to use names and ask for contact.

The objection may be raised that we, who do not have autism, have the real vision of the world, a world that is unpredictable. It is unrealistic to expect society to offer special protection for people with autism. It is our job to steer them towards being able to adapt to our world. But such a suggestion presupposes that a person with autism starts on a level playing field in sensory terms. It makes no allowance for the fragmented kaleidoscopic perceptions which may be painful and do not allow a person to make sense of the environment. Even laying aside humane considerations, the question we have to answer is: 'Which system works for *this* individual?'

Instead of expecting people to conform to our world, we need to enter theirs and understand their difficulties, simplify and structure their environment so that they are not constantly being overwhelmed by sensory and emotional overload. Then, within their terms, we may be able to move together into a wider variety of experience.

Summary

- We need to become fluent in all aspects of a person's language – the way they reassure themselves

- We need to learn to use parts of a person's language in a different context – 'copy and paste' – so that it can 'hold and deliver' our communications

- It is crucial that once we have set up a system which reassures a person, we do not remove it as they apparently improve. The autism is not 'cured'; rather, the environment has been made more sympathetic. We may need to maintain a buffer zone

- We must continue to understand the problems the person is experiencing

You Don't Know What It's Like

Section 14

'A SAFE BOX AND A SCARY BOX'
Containment and holding

We often work with people who have great difficulties in communicating from their world of sensory and emotional instability. In some situations, we have no way of unravelling the complexities of their distress. We may lack the therapeutic skill or the damage may be too great. Furthermore, in order to protect themselves, families may develop delicate webs of interaction which are difficult to explore. If these webs are broken, it will not just be the individual who is exposed. There is a real danger that the whole support system will break down.

Occasionally we hear outbursts from the depths of extreme distress dragging their undertones of isolation: *'You don't know what it's like.'*

We can only agree and feel the separation. There is a chasm between us and we shall never experience what they do, not as equals. But sometimes we can help people through a technique known as containment which seeks to encapsulate and disarm the bad things of which they are afraid (and which they feel may overwhelm them). We can also hold on to and keep safe the precious objects, objects that are so precious because they form the link between dependency and independence. These are the transitional objects that Winnicott describes.[38]

Holding anticipation and fear

When bad things happen in our lives, we are not only upset when they happen, we are also afraid that they may happen again. Our feelings are not just about danger but about fear – and this fearful anticipation can be as bad as an actual event. Jolliffe says that she is so conditioned by this fear that she lives in anticipation of some terrible event.[9]

Containment is a technique which uses **resonant images** to disarm the fear. While containment does not eliminate the actual cause of the danger, it may reduce stress by domesticating the co-existent fear.

In the history of Jeff below, he uses a box so that he can protect his belongings and feel that he is more in control of his life.

> **JEFF is obsessed by blood, dentists, clinics and drills. He is extremely restless and will not settle down to any activity. I suggest that we have two boxes, a 'safe' box and a 'scary' box. We draw pictures of images, some of which he finds scary. We cut them out and together put them in the appropriate boxes. Jeff learns to distinguish between the safe box and the scary box. He is fascinated by our task and it holds his attention.**

Similar work was done with a child who walked round the house holding her 'box of scary things', which she had helped to draw and cut out. When she rattled it she could hear them inside her box. This did not take away the things she was scared of, but gave her some control over them. It domesticated them.

There are many ways we can use to hold and contain situations. In *Person to Person*, I describe drawing road plans with **George** who has severe autism. He is fixated on them to the exclusion of other activities. Once he has enough space in the form of a very large piece of paper, he is happy to share this activity but feels threatened when, attempting to broaden the interaction, I add cars. George's distress is contained when we add a car park and park the cars firmly in it. This is an image in his language and it neutralises the onset of disturbed behaviour. (It is not necessary to remove the cars.) In a world that is unpredictable, once the cars are parked, they are no longer unpredictable – they are no longer a threat. In other words, we are cutting down on George's stress by containing unpredictability.

Another way to hold things which pose a threat because of the demands they make is to put them on a computer. In an interview, Donna Williams tells us that although she can handle questions put to her through a computer, she cannot manage it when the interviewer asks her a direct question.[16] Similarly, Lindsey Weeks expresses a preference for the computer:

> *'It's nothing personal. I just cannot handle the face-to-face communication.'* [11]

You Don't Know What It's Like

The computer can also be used as a box to hold the unspeakable. We tried this with Liza (see page 63) and she was at least able to write the word 'pull' that she found so intolerable, without becoming disturbed.

If we remember what Jolliffe says about the threat which reality poses to her – when she describes her escalating fear of 'objects, objects that move, and objects that move and make a noise'[9] we realise that almost anything can be scary for a person with autism, particularly when they are children and have not yet been able to build up any defence mechanisms. This may make it extremely difficult for them to learn, since the list of frightening objects can include the most basic objects used as educational equipment, such as bricks, pencils and pens. However, we can sometimes make these objects safe by 'holding' them in the stereotype. In *Person to Person*, I describe the history of a child who is fixated on 'Mummy's blue car' – she cannot say anything else until I make her a large wooden car, two sides with a box between. Now she can use and name bricks and other objects, provided they are 'in the car'. The stereotype holds the objects and renders them safe. They are non-threatening and will not cause overload or fragmentation in the child's brain.

In **Section 2**, I described how it was possible to shift the verbally offensive language of a young man by accepting it cheerfully and 'holding' it for him, when ignoring it had not had a positive outcome. Trapped in an emotional tangle, he needed a way out and the surprise evoked by laughing and agreeing with him was enough to move him beyond his behavioural dysfunction in our relationship.

Holding precious objects

We can actually make boxes, not just to disarm the scary things but also to hold and protect a person's precious objects. This is also described in *Person to Person* but here I want to look in more detail at the motivation which leads people to carry round their possessions with them and sometimes become extremely disturbed if they are removed.

To begin with, this type of protection may be simply about providing a secure place to keep objects which are otherwise likely to be taken by others – a not uncommon situation where doors are unlocked and individuals may lack any sense of private property.

> **FAY lives in an assessment unit and, although she has her own bedroom, at times, depending on the shifting balance of men and women in the house, she is sometimes moved out. She cannot really call her room her own and feels sufficiently insecure to carry around with her all her toiletries in plastic bags. She cannot manage a key.**

> In the workshop, we make a box large enough to contain Fay's bottles and tins and design a specially adapted locking mechanism. To open it, all Fay has to do is to push a pencil through a small hole against a flap of stiff plastic which hooks over a peg inside. This releases the lid. She now has a container she can open but others cannot. She can keep her precious things safely.

In some cases a person's choice of precious objects may seem bizarre to our eyes. In *Person to Person* I explore the history of Jim, who desperately desires pieces of plastic to the point of breaking up furniture and bringing endless trouble on himself in order to obtain them. As the pieces are removed, he eats them in order to retain them. His need overrides all attempts to divert or control his behaviour. Everything Jim does is focused on this end.

In order to see why this is so, we need to look more closely at what is meant by 'transitional objects' and understand the power that is vested in them.

Transitional objects

Transitional objects are part of the normal process of the development that all of us share. When we are born, we are totally dependent on our mothers and we believe everything is part of ourselves – we do not distinguish anything from ourselves, there is no such thing as 'other'. To put it personally, growth of my sense of 'self' outwards involves my learning to distinguish what is my 'self' and what is not 'myself', between 'me' and 'not me'. By continuous testing, my brain works out what is part of me and what is not. I learn to separate myself from my mother and move towards independence. Transitional objects are special objects which are part of the complex process of separation. They stand halfway between dependence on the mother and her breast, and independence and the development of a sense of self.[22]

When we see toddlers sucking their fingers or clutching teddy bears and putting disintegrating bits of blanket in their mouths, it is difficult for us to recall the urgency that attended such objects. We were, quite literally, lost without them. Groping our way into a world which was unpredictable and sometimes appeared hostile and rejected us, these objects were stepping stones from total dependency on our mothers to independence. They were objects of security to which we could withdraw before returning to the struggle to make sense of the world into which we had been thrown. They were oases where we could retreat to suck the comforting breast substitute, biding our time until we had strength to return to our onslaught on reality.

If all is well, the child becomes stronger. As the objects in which they have vested so much attention fall apart, they move on, passing to another developmental stage. Sometimes, however, when the battle is too hard, the child bears scars which send him running for security later in life. If the struggle to separate themselves is too great, children may give up the battle to move on. They retain the need for objects of security.

Many people with very severe learning impairment have great difficulty moving through the developmental stages which are common to all of us. The next history (as also described in *Getting in Touch*) illustrates the plight of a woman in her early twenties who clearly is caught up in the need for a breast substitute. She has not outgrown the need to be fed and protected by her mother, not so much in a physical but in a psychological sense.

> **NORAH collects plastic sacks which she rolls into a ball, regurgitates on and sucks. She is deeply upset if they are removed and will break open cupboards to acquire another, fighting off anyone who tries to stop her. The intensity of her struggle is of the order of a 'life and death response'. She feels so threatened by the outside world that her existence is at stake – she needs the sacks in order to survive. She is so locked into this need that it excludes the possibility of all other ways of responding to external reality.**

Not all transitional objects are so obviously related to the breast and maternal security. With Norah, the relationship is easy to see; however, sometimes it is difficult for us to understand why an individual chooses a particular object to fixate on – we cannot see its fascination. The object has no power for us and may even be disagreeable. However, it is recognisable as more than just an entity by the attraction it holds for an individual and their response to it.

How can we help a person who is caught in this developmental stage to grow through it? Anyone who has witnessed the outcome of trying to remove a child's teddy will be aware that we cannot 'frogmarch' a person to independence by removing the object on which they are dependent. They simply become more desperate for it; their dependency increases rather than decreases. We have to look for creative ways of working with people in the stage they are in.

I was able to begin working with Norah using a large wooden ball which was smooth and comfortable to hold. It is a breast-shaped object and has weight. She enjoys holding it. Gradually, I encouraged her to place it in a bucket and then to post it through a bucket with a hole in its lid. Now, sometimes she has it and sometimes not – but at the same time as letting it go, she knows where it is and can anticipate finding it. To the pleasure of security, we have added the spice of excitement. When we take off the lid it is still there, but Norah's security is no longer dependent on holding the ball all the time. She can let it go and still be safe.

Before we exclude ourselves from what we see as childish behaviour related to transitional objects, we should remember our soft toys, our lucky charms and probably, in addition to its biochemical lure, the draw of cigarettes. A transitional object has power over and above its natural qualities.

Summary

We can:

- use holding techniques to preserve precious objects and disarm threatening objects
- acknowledge the power of transitional objects
- help people to move on through developmental stages.

You Don't Know What It's Like

Section 15

'DIFFICULT' BEHAVIOUR
Rewiring the brain

This section draws on *The Emotional Brain* by Le Doux.[37]

In the past, people considered the brain as the organ they thought with. Emotion was a matter for the heart. Now, neurobiologists are beginning to unravel our emotional responses as part of brain function. The idea of the emotional brain is new. Put simply, there is a hot-line from the senses – the eyes, ears, touch, taste, smell and balance – to the amygdala. The amygdala is an organ about the size of an almond in the mid-lower brain. In emergencies, it takes responsibility for organising responses, turning on the adrenaline, raising our heartbeat and generally preparing us for the freeze, flight or fight options. Afterwards, we may reflect: *'We never had time to think about it.'*

In a sense this is true: the thinking part of our brains was not invoked. The pathway from the eyes to the amygdala is faster than that from the eyes (if sight was the sense which perceived the danger) to the thinking brain. The thinking brain comes into play later. Like it or not, when the amygdala perceives danger, we find ourselves in the position of a learner driver in a dual control car. The instructor overrides any action we might have taken, setting up responses designed to get us out of trouble. The few milliseconds saved may have made the difference between life and death. The part of the brain which makes conscious decisions has not been involved.

Whether or not we have impairment, we all respond to situations we find stressful – but the level at which an emotional response is triggered in any particular individual varies over a wide range. I may be terrified by an event that leaves you unmoved or we may both be scared of the same situation; even so, I may be much more afraid than you are and so respond earlier or more violently. Whether or not I react is dependent on whether I have 'learned' to link a particular situation with danger – if I have, I will react to it (or to long-term memories of objects I associate with the danger). I will carry the anxiety, and anything that reminds me of the situation will trigger stress and responses, even if I am not consciously aware of the source of my fear. This makes the system unreliable in terms of what is happening *now*. Responses may be triggered by an event or an emotional memory that accompanied the original trauma so that I may be reacting to something that happened a long time ago. As far as an outsider can see, there may be no obvious connection between outburst and a cause. Le Doux says that these (to our mind) irrational triggers are extremely difficult to extinguish. We need to look at a person's life to reduce their incidence. It is no use saying that the person needs to get used to the triggers. This may not be possible.

We need to distinguish between our *immediate* responses to such outbursts, dealing with situations as they arise, and our *long-term* strategies to try to reduce the incidence of factors which are acting as the triggers to disturbed behaviour. For example, if we know a person is upset by the colour red, we shall avoid wearing it. When we are faced with an immediate escalation of disturbed behaviour, Bennett discusses techniques we can use which are based on our understanding of the biological processes which are going on during the onset and build-up of aggression – and also the effect that a particular response will have, in biological terms, on that deteriorating behaviour.

Bennett discusses the characteristic stages of the fight response (triggering, build-up, crisis, recovery and post-event depression), the corresponding levels of arousal and the signs by which we can recognise these, so that our responses can be appropriate and not escalate the situation further. For example, Bennett points out that one of the effects of adrenaline build-up is to impair the ability to hear, decode and interpret language and speech – so a person may physically be unable to respond. They simply cannot co-operate: by expecting them to do so we are increasing stress and the flow of adrenaline.

In this book we have looked at various creative techniques that are useful in working with people whose stress causes them to behave in ways that we find difficult to handle. Through increasing our understanding of the circumstances which trigger 'difficult behaviour', we have been able to examine alternative ways of working with causes, such as:

1 **Intensive Interaction** (becoming fluent in people's own language)

2 the creative use of **resonant images** (images that trigger understanding and evoke positive feelings such as increasing confidence and feelings of wellbeing)

3 the uses of **surprise in a non-threatening context**

4 '**copy and paste**': the ability to shift an element of a person's language which carries a positive load and use it where they are distressed (neutralising negative feelings)

You Don't Know What It's Like

5 **'gift wrapping'**: surrounding information in our language with elements of a person's own language (neutralising information that might otherwise be perceived as threatening)

6 **using a person's language** to re-establish contact between the inner and outer world when they have become locked into escalating disturbed behaviours

7 **containment through holding** (making things less frightening or preserving precious things).

All these approaches require complete attention to the individual in a therapeutic way, trying to understand their life as they see it and not as we react to it. We must learn to respect all the anxieties gathered from a person's encounters during reality testing, the blueprints from experiences that happened in the past and how these interact with current encounters with the outside world. We must also pay regard to their hypersensitivities.

I want to try to look more deeply at what it is we are doing when we say we are working therapeutically to reduce stress. Le Doux says:

> 'Psychoanalytic theory and conditioning theories assume that anxiety is the result of traumatic learning experiences that foster the establishment of anxiety-producing long-term memories. In this sense, psychoanalytic and conditioning theory have drawn the similar conclusions about the origins of anxiety. Psychoanalysis seeks to help make the patient conscious of the origins of inner conflict (helping them to become conscious of what was theirs but they had not known before and therefore making it possible for them to take responsibility for it. See **Section 8**: 'The lady with the knife'), *whereas behaviour therapy tries to rid the person of the symptoms of anxiety, often through various forms of extinction therapy – with the aim of unlearning the negative emotional reaction.'* (Page 263)

That is, the aim of behaviour therapy is to raise the level at which an emotional response is triggered by neutralising the occasions that cause it: if I no longer feel threatened by something, I shall not need to react to it.

Again, Le Doux says:

> 'Therapy is just another way of synaptic potentiation in brain pathways that control the amygdala. The amygdala's emotional memories are indelibly burned into its circuits. The best we can do is to regulate their expression and the way we do this is by getting the cortex to control the amygdala.' (Page 265)

In other words, we need to find ways of rewiring the brain. To make it more difficult, we are trying to do this with people who have limited or no verbal skills. All we have to go on is our power of observation, our creative skills and the general rule that we are seeking to reduce anxiety and stress at the same time as improving self-confidence. However, we have some powerful tools: the techniques afforded by Intensive Interaction and by using images that resonate for an individual. While these techniques lie outside the normal scope of psychoanalysis and cognitive therapy, they can have parallel effects in areas which would normally be considered inaccessible due to the depth of impairment.

Summary

We need to consider:

- the hot-line from the senses – the part played by the amygdala
- reducing the triggers if we can see what they are
- creative ways of approaching stress
- whether we can rewire the brain.

Section 16

'BIT'
Transitional phenomena
and reducing stress

How can we bring order and meaning to people whose sensory lives are chaotic?

Reading accounts of childhood autism, one is struck by the use of such expressions as 'terror' and 'agony' – extreme words used by people to try to give us an idea of the painful ordeals and danger of extinction that they perceive. Small wonder that they may respond with violent behaviour which we do not know how to contain – just as they cannot contain the violence of these assaults on their senses. Existing in a world without parameters, these people may have nothing to cling to but a few repetitive behaviours or objects on which they are fixated, activities which bring them some relief from the onslaught of their senses by raising the level of endorphins (the body's natural pain-killers) in the brain.

> **MANDY is six. She has severe autism and is very disturbed. At school, she has frequent outbursts in which she attacks staff or pupils. She has a toy rabbit which she calls 'Bit', which she does not bring to school. Her class has a number of other disturbed children and, because of this, in spite of the best efforts of the teacher, there is tension and noise in the classroom, with children moving about in ways that non-autistic children might find intimidating. Mandy draws well but her attention span is short and she has frequent tantrums.**

If we go back to what people with autism say about their sensory experiences, in her disorientated world, Mandy's safety is invested in 'Bit'. When she has hold of it, she knows what she is doing – she can physically feel herself hanging on to an object she recognises through touch. At school, she does not have that security.

I suggest to Mandy that we draw 'Bit'. She immediately focuses on this idea and produces a recognisable drawing which she colours in. We cut it out and paste it on card. The next time she is upset she says, 'Be good, have "Bit".'

Navigating the gap between self and other

When she is disturbed, Mandy needs the security offered by 'her object', that is, an unchanging object in a slippery world, the one thing she can physically hang on to and know where she is in relation to it: a life-belt in a stormy sea. 'Bit' offers comfort and security and fulfils an equivalent function to a transitional object. Although it may not have arisen directly during separation from the mother and establishment of the self as a separate entity, it does occupy the same niche. Winnicott extended the concept of the transitional object to transitional phenomena.[38] This includes anything which enables us to negotiate and navigate the gap between self and other – giving purchase on the unknown. Under this heading then, we can also, for example, include Mike's '-KS, -KS' – a verbal aid to making sense of his surroundings. Perhaps this is one way of thinking of some stereotypic behaviour.

In addition to this, we can not only use Mandy's 'Bit' to provide stability when she is upset, but also use it to focus her attention when she is calm – for example, 'Bit' can point out letters for reading. We can use the stereotype or fixations to maintain the position of objects that might otherwise 'move about' and therefore be seen as threatening. There is no associated anxiety that objects of fixation will slither around or alter dimensions. Temple Grandin is quite clear that such objects of fixation can be used to help teach children.[8] Provided that the teaching material is related to or incorporated into the stereotype, the stereotype will help to focus their attention and objects will remain unthreatening.

Grandin is less happy about the use of self-stimulatory behaviours in a similar way, while Gillingham urges that repetitive behaviours should be eliminated because, as well as protecting the individual from pain, the raised level of endorphins cuts the person off so that they are unable to respond to environment and people – they are lost in their own world.[15] However, Gillingham focuses on the need to reduce the level of sensory stimulation rather than trying to eliminate behaviours directly, since the latter process, if it is successful (and more often than not one eliminated repetitive behaviour is replaced by another), may leave an individual vulnerable to the stress and pain of fragmentation since they are denied the protection afforded by endorphins.

While agreeing completely with the need to reduce stimuli which are causing hypersensitivity, there is the practical problem that, for a variety of reasons, it is often very difficult to effect the conditions which would help this reduction. For example, in many centres as

You Don't Know What It's Like

they are currently designed, there is no possibility for the provision of a quiet room and also, at present, a lack of awareness that this may be crucial to a person's wellbeing. In an effort to construct an 'attractive and stimulating' environment, most rooms are cluttered with pictures and conflicting patterns and designs. Gillingham says we should *aim for tranquillity*. In this respect, we need to rethink the service provided for people with autism with all the implications for training that this brings, so that they can have somewhere in their lives to go when they are overloaded which will not make the problem worse. We also need to take active steps to ensure that their environment is modified so they are not subjected to stimuli that cause them pain.

At the time of writing, it is gradually becoming clear that the use of Irlen lenses may provide some people with ASD with the sensory tranquillity they require, not because they 'cut out' certain colours to which people are sensitive, but because they adjust the frequency of visual input so that it synchronises with the ability to process the input.

The other approach, which should be complementary to attention to hypersensitivities is, as we have discussed, the creative development and use of a person's language to attract their attention.

> *'Coming up with creative ways to use the obsessions of a student with autism is a challenge well worth facing. By using the interests of a child to motivate learning, we have the opportunity to build rather than destroy.'* [15]

Personal experience in working with people who have severe learning impairment as well as disorders within the autistic spectrum, suggests that there is little difference between using a person's fixations – for example, a fixation on bits of paper which are flapped in front of the face, and using self-stimulatory repetitive behaviours such as flapping fingers in front of the face as a basis for interaction. As I have suggested, fixations are not necessarily related to the outside world but, rather, to that part of the world which has been hijacked and brought in to be used as part of the furniture of the inner world.[1] Reflected back to a person, both fixations and self-stimulatory repetitive behaviours can give access to the inner world and allow a person to respond, since they do not trigger overload. Also, they retain their function of acting as a buffer between dysfunctional brain processing and those elements of the environment which disturb a person – even when bringing people out of their inner world.

Summary

This section looked at:

- bringing meaning to disordered perception; the stereotype as a transitional phenomenon

- reducing stress through paying attention to hypersensitivity and using an individual's language – a complementary approach.

Section 17

HOW CAN WE HELP?

How can we help people who have severe learning disabilities as well as autistic tendencies?

At present we cannot 'cure' autism, but we can improve the lives of those experiencing it by the use of techniques which have positive outcomes, remembering that each person with whom we work is different – we need to tease out individually-based strategies for each one. In effect, we need to make a complete inventory of each person's life, asking ourselves all the time how they experience it.

Take account of hypersensitivities

- Use a soft voice

- Let people know what we are going to do before we do it

- If there appears to be visual hypersensitivity, look at the possibility of using coloured Irlen lenses if this is a practical option. (Visual hypersensitivity is not about having bad eyesight.) Apart from the more obvious indications of hypersensitivity such as screwing up the eyes or preference for dim light or a certain colour, there may be more subtle indications. Among those which are currently being explored are situations which suggest a person is having difficulties with visual processing:

  - spitting on, and trying to erase, reflections on shining surfaces or dark knots in the wood of a table

  - having difficulty making choices (holding two or more images simultaneously)

  - having difficulties adapting to the unexpected or coping with change (trying to marry an anticipated image to an alternative one)

Reduce sensory input and particularly the personal threat posed by people

- Respect the space a person requires

Make a detailed and objective observation of the person's body/facial language and behaviours

- How do they 'talk' to themselves?

- What are they 'really' getting out of an activity? This may not be the same as they superficially seem to be getting out of it; we may need to try a behaviour ourselves in order to see what it is they are seeing. (A person twiddling a toy car as they look through it may actually be watching their face in its little window)

- How does the person respond to situations?

- How does the person 'talk' to us?

Remember that communication is not just about exchanging information but also about building relationships

- Work with *the person's* language to build mutual confidence and relatedness, giving them a chance to express feeling

Simplify and standardise communications so that a person can understand what we are trying to tell them

- Avoid abstract signs and minimise questions and choices

- Even if a person has some speech, it is often helpful to back up our information and requests by pictures or gestures and objects of reference (objects which are a recognisable part of the communication)

- If a person gets stuck when they are trying to do something, we need to remember that this may be because their motor system has become disconnected from the brain so that they cannot proceed. (There is a difference between knowing what we want to do and being able to do it.) The connection can often be re-established by the use of a relevant gesture or 'clue' through an alternative sense

Remember the difficulties that people have in working out what is going to happen and their inflexible and literal interpretations once they have managed to understand

- Try to avoid unanticipated changes which arise because a person cannot marry their picture of what *was* going to happen with what *is* happening

- If these situations do arise, use gesture and objects of reference, or pictures if they are understood, to help negotiate the unexpected

Help the person to know what is going to happen by introducing structures and timetables which are individually designed so that they will be able to make sense of them

- The distinction between what *is* happening and what is *going to* happen must be visually extremely clear. Kitchen timers can be used to help people to understand the difference between 'now' and 'not now'. The structured educational approach of the 'TEACCH' method (see **Resources**) is also helpful to children

- Once a helpful structure has been established, greatest caution should be exercised in trying to reduce it. Sudden reduction in the structure which supports a person may be catastrophic

- Give people time to process information

Managing a successful programme

Successful programmes are dependent on effective implementation. Listening to some of the managers of strategies which have had effective outcomes, the qualities they felt made for positive outcomes were:

- a management style which takes a pragmatic approach, creating an environment where it is possible to try out a strategy to see whether or not it is successful. Managers need to say, 'If it works, we will continue' and 'If it fails, we will reflect on why it is failing in a manner that is non-judgemental of staff'

- appointment of a change facilitator, a keyworker or primary nurse working within a team. This person is encouraged to come up with ideas and is supported by individual supervision

- staff being confident that, if they run into difficulties, leaders will support them with hands-on involvement, helping them to sort out the problems they encounter. These problems will be looked at, not just in the context of the service user, but also in terms of the interactions between support staff and user

- while theoretical background is important, managers need to emphasise the value of practical objectives such as, 'What we are going to do this week?'

- keyworkers being encouraged to spread effective ideas laterally through their team to ensure consistency.

Each step we take may seem a small one, but the effect can be cumulative and can transform the lives of people who are struggling to make sense of their environment.

Section 18

WHAT DO WE MEAN BY SUCCESS?

Until recently, we have tended to measure success in terms of improvements in skill, but many of the positive outcomes we have been discussing are subjective:

- A woman with cerebral palsy sits up, smiles and starts to look round at her surroundings. (There has been nothing in her life which has been powerful enough to motivate this before)

- A man with severe autism and disturbed behaviour becomes calmer and interacts with staff. His challenging behaviour decreases

- A man with severe challenging behaviour who eats plastic is able to grow through this developmental stage. He starts to interact with his peers, to the extent of organising them to play games with him

For people with ASD, we can draw up a generalised table of potentially successful outcomes using the approaches suggested in preceding sections.

Potentially successful outcomes for people with ASD

Working with the stereotype	Working against the stereotype
Simplifying demands and language used	**Controlling behaviour**
The person becomes calmer – relaxes	The person remains stressed
More friendly	Isolated – chooses solitude
Lively and engaged, more able to enjoy themselves	Withdrawn
Increase in eye-contact on own terms. Smiles and laughs	Avoids eye-contact
Initiates contact	Rejects contact
Sometimes becomes more fluent in our language. Uses more words	Continues minimal use of our language
Capacity to handle a wider range of situations improves	No flexibility
'Difficult' behaviour decreases. In addition, staff find person easier to handle when they are upset	Behaviour management remains a problem

The primary effect of the type of interventions we have looked at in this book has been emotional – a general loosening up as an individual becomes less stressed and more confident. This is noticeable for support staff who work with the individuals – they simply become warmer, easier and often more fun to work with.

However, it may be less easy to be objective about such improvements than simply deciding whether or not an individual can brush their hair or recognise colours. One of the questions we have to ask before we evaluate improvements is what human value we place on deepening the capacity for emotional interaction and awakening the capacity for joy. In case this should appear too ill-defined an objective, the ability to connect with people facilitates *everything* we do with each other.

Section 19

'BACK WHERE WE STARTED'
Reciprocal attempts to communicate

Failure to communicate is not the only factor underlying challenging behaviour. Hewett lists sixty-five in his book, *Challenging Behaviour*,[24] and even this extensive list does not include the difficulties and consequent behavioural problems which some women experience as a consequence of being unable to nurture.[1] Yet, in one way or another, failure to communicate does account for a large slice of challenging behaviour. How can we set up relationships if we cannot 'talk' to each other? It is easy to have low self-esteem if we live in a world from which we are excluded. We can fall into a pattern of fighting for our existence in a world where nothing makes sense so that we always feel threatened.

Because most of the work I am asked to do concerns ways of setting up communication, much of this book is about people with autism. However, in most cases, the attitudes and approaches which we have looked at apply within and outside the autistic spectrum.

We need to:

- work 'from' an individual rather than with them, looking at the world from their point of view and learning to use in a non-threatening way the language they have developed to talk to themselves and communicate with us

- simplify our language to a level at which a person is most easily able to understand it

- set up structures which present information that people can grasp in a way which is non-threatening.

All these techniques are universal and can be generally applied.

To end, I want to return, through a simple behaviour, to the dominant theme of this book – the need to learn that an individual's sensory experience may be totally different from ours and to look at their world through their eyes and ears and touch – their sensory experience. To do this, I should like to look at the experience of a staff support member who asked about a woman who was autistic and fixated on a certain drawer.

> **BERYL is fascinated by a drawer. A member of support staff says that he finds this inexplicable as Beryl apparently does not want anything out of the drawer but she is so desperate that she will climb over all manner of obstacles so that she can point her finger to it. I ask the support worker if he has ever tried pointing to it with her and he replies that he had once done this. He shows me how she turned to him, smiling and rubbing her hands together with pleasure.**

It seems that Beryl is fixated on an object to the exclusion of everything else. It dominates her thoughts and activities. To us, who are outsiders, there is no rational reason for an attachment we cannot share, even at second-hand when Beryl points it out to us. It is an impediment to a relationship, as well as being irritating when she goes on and on about it. But suppose we try looking at the drawer from Beryl's viewpoint. In order to do this, we need to go back to Sian Barron and what he says about his fixation with light switches:

- 'I know what I'm doing'

- 'It's the same every time'

- 'I feel secure when I'm doing it'[10]

It is now clear that what Beryl is doing is showing us and sharing what is, for her, the lynch-pin of her existence; in a world of sensory turmoil, it is the object that holds her life together. It is the most important thing she has and we need to show her that we have understood this and taken it on board. As soon as her keyworker shows her that he understands it is important to her, she is able to connect with him, and he with her. They share understanding. Hewett uses the word 'celebration' to underscore the process of valuing a person's responses and attempts to communicate.[26]

Value who the person is

We must value a person's precious objects and activities and be honoured by their sharing them with us because that is where they are centred. In valuing these, we value who the person is. Far from enhancing the behaviours we find unwelcome, the frequent outcome is that beyond impairment, in letting go, we reach each other in the deepest sense.

You Don't Know What It's Like

The theory of mind suggests that one of the characteristics of autism is that an individual is unable to put themselves in another's position and so lacks the ability to empathise with them. The person has no access to our complex world of social interaction and relationships. There is a gulf between their literal understanding and our more subtle grasp of motives. They do not understand how our world works. Ironically, if we are not careful, we fall into the same trap – we judge their world by ours.

Donna Williams is right – we need to let go of our presuppositions and ways of thinking, and all the blueprints we find so important, so that we can become travellers in the mind.

The liberation can be astonishing.

Section 20

A GP'S VIEWPOINT
By Dr Matt Hoghton

This chapter is dedicated to the memories of Alan Mundy, Hugh Davies and Tim Armstrong.

For several years, my work as a doctor has been with adults with severe and multiple profound learning disabilities. In common with many general practitioners, I have found myself meeting people with conditions such as autistic spectrum disorder (ASD) with which I had very little experience. I first came across the work of Intensive Interaction by chance, when a series of carers, nurses and doctors who had asked for help with difficult problems, particularly with regard to communication and challenging behaviour, suggested I talk to Phoebe Caldwell. Having read her previous suggestions in the notes of my clients, and seen her work on video, I began to realise that not only should we be interested in improving our clients' living conditions but, more fundamentally, should begin to achieve a meaningful interpersonal two-way contact. I started to see that doctors share the prejudices and ignorance about ASD which are often found among the general population.

As doctors, we expect to help other people, and other people expect us to help them. This may make it difficult for us to acknowledge when we find we have inadequate skills. Using Intensive Interaction has helped me to redefine my relationship with people with ASD and think of myself as an assistant rather than a carer. As a carer, I am invested with personal power over an individual but, as an assistant, the relationship is more balanced. Working with someone with ASD can be difficult; neither those intimately caring, nor the professionals, have a monopoly on the answers. The best results are only obtained when those involved work together and pool their experience.

When one starts to train as a health care worker, one has only a small amount of experience from which to work. Initially, most of my diagnosis and problem solving was based on trying to work things out from first principles. However, growing experience, coupled with pressure of time, resulted in diagnoses which relied on pattern recognition. (This is helpful as it speeds up the process of health care but gets in the way when you meet individuals who do not fit the norm.) People with autism and some people with challenging behaviour do not fit easily into patterns. This is particularly true of ASD and most of us struggle to understand its complex manifestations.

Apart from the knowledge gap, we have considerable communication difficulties. If a person is unable to communicate in our language, we often try to impose other languages (such as sign) on them, rather than simply trying to use their language. Most people with autism are able to communicate in their own language but we fail to observe it, recognise its importance and use it to engage their attention. Intensive Interaction allows us to observe, watch and reflect back to people their own language. Using this interpersonal approach enables us to connect and engage with people. Simply taking time to watch someone move, listen to their sounds, and reflect these back to them will start the process (and this does not require years of training to do). Most people will stop and notice when I use their language.

In my experience of teaching medical students, they can learn the necessary skills to get in touch with people with ASD without too much difficulty. They are often delighted with the reaction they get. I show them that they can continue to hold an individual's attention by building on their responses to set up a conversation without words and I emphasise to the students the importance of listening for responses. The empathy generated can change the relationship from an unknown stranger to a friend.

JOHN is a 24-year-old man with learning difficulties who is unwell. I am anxious, as I have heard he is difficult to examine and is sometimes aggressive, especially if he is having blood taken. He is the first person I have tried to communicate with in his language. He is sitting by his bed on the floor cross-legged without any shoes on. I sit down opposite him and adopt the same position. He then starts rocking his upper body and snorting through his nostrils. I copy his behaviour and then he stops and watches me. I then stop and he restarts. We then take it in turns to 'speak' to each other. In ten minutes, he is letting me examine him. I do not push my luck with blood-taking on this occasion but return the following week to pick up where we have left off. John and I are now good friends and he educates me regularly in the latest pop music. Working together with his carers has helped me to deepen my relationship with John. We both trust each other. I trust John will not hurt me or break my spectacles and I think he trusts me to work with him as a practitioner.

You Don't Know What It's Like

Many of us are frightened of working with people with ASD. Where there should be trust, we feel alienated. Our fears derive from misconceptions, a lack of familiarity and knowledge. Our fundamental skills of flexibility and intuition need to replace the pattern recognition previously mentioned. Lovett says we need to develop a new respect for the intuitive.[39]

Who has ASD?

Wing found in 1989 that one-third of the residents of an adult mental handicap hospital had ASD, whilst previous research has shown that 78% of those with ASD also had severe learning disabilities.[40,41] As Gould says:

> 'Some children are very disabled with low level of functioning. Others have superior intelligence with very high levels of skills in certain areas.' [42]

One of the difficulties is that this first group is usually treated as 'people with learning disabilities', sometimes with challenging behaviour, rather than people who come within the umbrella of ASD. This means that their autistic features are often ignored. I agree with Gould when she says:

> 'It is essential that the autism is recognised since it has important implications for treatment and prognosis.' [42]

Some of the people who come and see me have very severe learning disabilities as well as presenting the behaviours and special needs which are also characteristic of people who have autism or Asperger's syndrome as at present defined. Most of the work which has been done seems to have been focused on high-functioning people – little appears to have been published in relation to people who are low-functioning and whose autism is linked with such disabilities as:

- Down's syndrome
- cerebral palsy
- general learning disabilities
- Fragile X syndrome
- Rett's syndrome.

When Kanner first described it in 1943, the incidence of autism was believed to be one in 5,000 live births.[43] Since then, there appears to be a marked increase in the incidence of autism with reports in the Brick township, New Jersey, USA, of one in 150 live births and the Eureka school district California of one in 132. There are problems interpreting the data as the definition of the diagnosis and awareness among clinicians has changed but there is an apparent dramatic rise in the number of people, especially boys, affected.

Causes and diagnosis

At present, although we still do not know what causes ASD, our view is changing. We know that the urine of people with ASD contains high levels of the breakdown products of opioid peptides from the blood. These opioid peptides are toxic to brain tissue and would disrupt the normal functioning of the central nervous system. It is thought that the high levels of these potent substances may be due to a variety of problems, particularly if the barrier of the intestine is breached. The theory of the leaky bowel suggests that this is allowing more peptides to cross the gut wall into the bloodstream (See **Diagram 1** below).

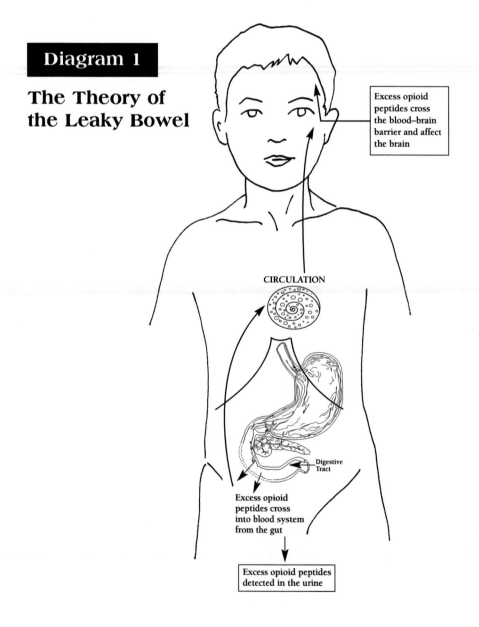

Diagram 1

The Theory of the Leaky Bowel

Excess opioid peptides cross the blood–brain barrier and affect the brain

CIRCULATION

Digestive Tract

Excess opioid peptides cross into blood system from the gut

Excess opioid peptides detected in the urine

You Don't Know What It's Like

One hypothesis is that giving together childhood vaccines such as mumps, measles and rubella (MMR) may induce a chronic immune response, which damages the boundary between the gut wall and bloodstream. At present, there is scant evidence for this and these childhood conditions are important causes of death and disability. As a variety of clinical specialists' research focuses on autism, the complex riddle of whether it is a metabolic, neuro-immunological, genetic or environmental disease is starting to unravel.

When it comes to diagnosis, there are two important scientific validated sets of criteria used to define ASD. They are rather similar but, although helpful in research and confirmation of diagnosis, may not be so helpful in early diagnosis. By the time the child has reached the psychiatrist, it is often fairly clear whether the child has a ASD or not. The National Autistic Society produces a useful guide for health professionals.

Classically, autism covers the triad of impairments of:

- social interaction

- social communication

- imagination.

However, excessive behaviour and symptoms often present early in childhood and these should be a cause for concern:

- **Self-stimulatory behaviour**

  This is often stereotyped and repetitive behaviour such as opening and shutting doors, flushing the toilet repeatedly, head banging, self-injury, rocking when standing from front to back foot, teeth grinding and repetitive noises.

- **Aggression**

  This can be difficult to manage as the child's physical size and strength increases. Parents often experience difficulties with boys over six years of age.

- **Hyperactivity**

  Children will lack awareness of personal safety and require considerable supervision to prevent injury, especially if they run away. The focus on the child may put other children in the family at risk with lack of attention.

- **Hypersensitivity to stimuli (hyperacusis)**

  Sound, colours and other visual stimuli have been reported as being overwhelming for some people. Similarly, light touch may cause disturbance but often firm pressure is well tolerated and can even be calming.

- **Bowel disturbances**

  Constipation and diarrhoea can both occur.

- **Sleep disturbances**

  These can upset and severely disturb family life.

- **Excessive eating or drinking (polydipsia)**

- **Clumsiness**

- **Special skills**

  About 10% of children with autism may have a skill disproportionate to their other abilities, such as in music, art, calculations or memory recall.

Other parents report a pale complexion with dark rings around the eyes and burning feelings often affecting the tips of the ears.

In the UK, it is essential to obtain a strict diagnosis in order to access the limited specialised psychiatric and educational supports. It is clear that early intervention is needed but in order to get the 'passport' to resources, you need a firm diagnosis. Access to getting this diagnosis is often restricted by resources, so parents have to maintain sustained pressure in order to achieve the best they can for their children.

Potential hopes

Autism can present as so difficult for parents to manage that it is very tempting to grasp any new hopeful possibilities. As this book goes to press there is, in addition to the interpersonal approaches we have looked at:

- the use of tinted **Irlen lenses** (originally developed for people with dyslexia) which is certainly helping some higher functioning people with their visual disturbance. Scotopic sensitivity causes a visual perceptual problem when viewing their environment. Various aspects of light, including intensity and wavelength, can trigger it. We are just beginning to explore the potential of these lenses for people with ASD, particularly with those who are less able

- the chance discovery of the effect of **secretin** when a young child, Parker Beck, had an endoscopy in 1996. There was such a dramatic improvement that other parents wanted their child to receive the drug. A number of parents report dramatic improvement in the USA. In 1999, the *Tonight* programme reported on Billy Tommey, the first child in the UK to receive secretin. The video showed considerable improvement in social communication and language ability. A six-year-old child with ASD on the programme reported that, 'My head feels better' and stopped his challenging behaviour.

There is at present considerable interest in secretin, a hormone produced by the small intestine, which helps to neutralise the acidity of stomach contents when they pass into the duodenum so that they can be acted on by enzymes from the pancreas.

The Ferring company has been manufacturing secretin, derived from pigs, for testing the function of the pancreas. As children with autism often have watery diarrhoea, it was tried – but there was no long-term effect on gastrointestinal functioning. However, after several days, there was apparent considerable improvement in communication and behaviour.[45]

According to the theory of opioid excess of autism, the condition is caused by excess of opioid neuropeptides that are harmful to normal brain function. Potential methods of reducing these effects are:

- to remove these from the diet; for example, using gluten-free and casein-free diets (The neuropetides may be produced by inadequate enzyme breakdown of gluten from wheat, rye and oats or casein from milk and other dairy products)

or

- to increase the enzyme activity of peptide digestion, which secretin does.

Secretin may also affect the brain directly by increasing the neurotransmitter, serotonin. So far there have only been some small studies showing potential benefits of single doses of pig-derived secretin given intravenously. There is also an oral version but as yet no scientific publications confirm claims for its efficacy and safety.

The structure of human secretin differs slightly from pig secretin. There are potential risks in the development of antibodies in using pig-derived secretin and some anecdotal evidence to suggest that allergic reactions may be serious. Worldwide supplies of porcine secretin have been depleted and the company Repligen has secured the worldwide rights to produce a synthetic human form of the drug.[45] The company has applied to the FDA (the Federal Drugs Administration in the USA) for New Drug Application (NDA) to start clinical trials to evaluate the effects of multiple doses of human secretin over a prolonged period. At present, there is a gap in supplies the drug has to be evaluated, as we don't know what the long-term side-effects may be.

There are two important principles when considering any medication for people with ASD:

- Side-effects are more common and poorly tolerated. It is important to introduce medication at a low dose and slowly build up. Recommended dose ranges are not available for children and adolescents. Medication should involve close co-operation between the individual, carers, and the prescriber, with regular review

- Medication may divert attention and focus from more important therapies, such as a structured environment and behavioural interventions

So far there is no evidence that any other medication modifies the disease of autism. There have been claims for anti-fungals, low-dose Naltroxene, and Vitamin B6, but research has not substantiated the initial promise.

As mentioned above, the introduction of gluten-free and casein-free diets can help reduce excess opioid neuropeptides. Before starting on these diets its is important to make sure that the person does not have coeliac disease. This can be screened for with a blood test for anti-endomysial and anti-gliadin antibodies. It is easier if you get dietary advice on how to try elimination diets for gluten (which is found in wheat, barley and rye) and casein (which is found in milk-based products). Keeping to diets is hard for all of us but may be particularly difficult if a person with autism is getting endorphins from that food. If you are able to keep the diet going, improvement should occur in approximately two weeks. If there is no improvement, the diet should not be persisted with.

The most important realisation has been that early intervention is essential in the development of social skills. PEACH and the EarlyBird Project (see **Resources**) have developed good practice with particular regard to the pre-school and primary years but these services are patchy across the UK. The focus now is on assessment and treatment of skill deficits, particularly in communication and language and minimising dangerous or disruptive behaviours. As a local doctor, I have found it important to try to link people as soon as possible to the available resources – especially other parents.

The future

Parents, other carers and people with ASD have fought to get the medical and scientific communities interested in this condition. A commercial (Johnson & Johnson) urine test is in development and will soon be available; this should allow diagnosis and home monitoring of the condition. I feel that ASD diagnosis and treatment may follow a similar pattern to the treatment of other metabolic diseases such as diabetes.

(Initially diabetes was thought to be a psychological disease until the metabolic basis of hyperglycaemia (high blood sugar levels) was discovered. Once the disease could be monitored it became more fully understood and better treatment developed. My hope is that the encouraging evidence for a similar mechanism of raised substances, that is neuropeptides in Autism, will lead us to being able to monitor the effects and evaluate new treatments.)

Exciting as these developments may be, I believe all progress starts with establishing communication and creating a caring relationship with people. We may take time to develop skills in interpreting behaviour but we must not be afraid of trying simple reflection – copying the person's behaviour and reflecting it back to them in a modified form. Inhibitions and embarrassment may prevent us if we think we will look silly but, once we experience the bond which an interpersonal approach helps us to establish, we will never look back. This type of intervention works with any age and is so important in our multicultural society.

Until now, the focus has been on children with ASD but without learning disabilities. We must champion communication and help for the silent ones, the non-verbal ones with learning disabilities and autism. We need to use these small bricks of knowledge to build the wall of progress. ASD is sometimes referred to as the invisible disability in people with learning disabilities. It is now time to make it visible.

References

1 Caldwell, P. A. with Stevens, P. (1998) *Person to Person*. Brighton: Pavilion Publishing.

2 Dunbar, R. (1997) *Grooming, Gossip and the Origin of Language*. London: Faber and Faber.

3 Bennett, L. (1998) *Making Sense of Violent Behaviour*. SLD Experience 22. Kidderminster: BILD.

4 Williams, D. (1996) *Autism – An Inside-Out Approach*. London and Bristol: Jessica Kingsley Publishers.

5 Emblem, B. *et al.* (1998) *The Challenge of Class Six in Challenging Behaviour*. (Ed. D. Hewett.) London: David Fulton Publishers.

6 Williams, D. (1992) *Nobody Nowhere*. London: Doubleday.

7 Williams, D. *Jam-Jar*. Channel 4 Film.

8 Grandin, T. & Scariano, M. (1986) *Emergence Labelled Autistic*. New York. Warner.

9 Jolliffe, T., Lansdown, R. & Robinson, C. (1992) Autism: A personal account. *Communication* **26** (3).

10 Barron, J. & Barron, S. (1992) *There's a Boy in Here*. New York: Simon and Schuster.

11 Weekes, L. *A Bridge of Voices*. Documentary. Radio 4.

12 Grant, L. (1998) *Remind Me Who I Am Again*. Cambridge: Granta.

13 O'Brian, A. (1988) In a private communication.

14 Grandin, T. (1995) *Thinking in Pictures*. New York: Doubleday.

15 Gillingham, G. (1995) *Autism: Handle With Care.* Tacit Publishing Inc, 8744–81 Ave, Edmonton, Alberta T6C OW6, Canada.

16 Williams, D. NBC Film.

17 Arnall, D. & Peters, J. (1992) *A is for Autism.* London: A Finetake Production for BBC Radio 4.

18 Williams, D. (1996) *Like Colour To the Blind.* New York: Time Books/Random House.

19 Warburton, J. *A Bridge of Voices.* Radio 4.

20 Eardley, J. (1988) In a private communication.

21 Davis, M. & Wallbridge, D. (1990) *Boundary and Space: An Introduction to the Work of D. W. Winnicott.* London: H. Karnac Books Ltd.

22 Stern, D. (1985) *The Interpersonal World of the Infant.* London: Basic Books/ Harper Collins.

23 Lovett, H. (1985) *Cognitive Counselling and People with Special Needs.* Eastbourne: Prager.

24 Culshaw, T. & Purvis, P. (1998) Developing Practice in a Residential Team. In: D. Hewett (Ed) *Challenging Behaviour.* London: David Fulton Publishers, Ltd.

25 Ephraim, G. W. (1986) *A Brief Introduction to Augmented Mothering.* Playtrack Pamphlet, Harperbury Hospital, Radlett, Herts.

26 Nind, M. & Hewett, D. (1994) *Access to Communication.* London: David Fulton Publishers, Ltd.

27 Hewett, D. & Nind, M. (1998) *Interaction in Action.* London: David Fulton Publishers, Ltd.

28 Ware, J. (1997) *Educating Children with Profound and Multiple Learning Difficulties.* London: David Fulton Publishers, Ltd.

29 Caldwell, P. (1996) *Getting in Touch.* Brighton: Pavilion Publishing/Joseph Rowntree Foundation.

30 Ephraim, G. (1994) In a private communication.

31 DeBono, E. (1983) *Atlas of Management Thinking.* London: Penguin Books.

You Don't Know What It's Like

32 Peeters, T. (1997) *Autism: From Theoretical Understanding to Educational Intervention.* London: Whurr Publishers.

33 Guess, D. *et al.* (1985) Concepts and issues related to choice making and autonomy among persons with severe disabilities. *Journal of Association of Persons with Severe Handicaps* **10** (2).

34 Williams, H. & Jones, R. P. S. (1997) Teaching Cognitive Self-regulation of Independence and Emotion Control Skills. In: S. E. Kroese, D. Dagnan & K. Loumidis (Eds) *Cognitive Behaviour Therapy for People with Learning Disabilities.* London: Routledge.

35 Swain, J. (1989) Learned helplessness theory and people with learning difficulties: the psychological price of powerlessness. In: A. Brechin & J. Walmsley (Eds) *Making Connections.* London: Hodder and Stoughton.

36 Baker, S. (1997) *PECS: The Picture Exchange Communication System.* West Sussex Educational Psychology and Portage Service.

37 Le Doux, J. (1998) *The Emotional Brain.* London: Weidenfeld and Nicolson.

38 Winnicott, D. W. (1971) *Playing and Reality.* London: Routledge.

39 Lovett, H. (1995) Video. Bolton Institute of Higher Education. Inclusive Education Conference.

40 Wing, L. (1989) *Hospital Closure and the Effects on Residents.* Aldershot: Avebury Press.

41 Wing, L. & Gould, J. (1979) Severe impairments of social interaction and associated abnormalities in children: epidemiology and classification. *Journal of Autism and Developmental Disorders* **9** (1) 11–29.

42 Gould, J. (1999) *Recognising Autism. The Autistic Spectrum: A handbook.* London: The National Autistic Society.

43 Kanner, L. (1943) Autistic disturbances of affective contact. *Nervous Child* **2** 217–500.

44 Horvath, K., Stefanatos, G., Sokolski, K. N., Wachtel, R., Nabors L. & Tildon, J. T. (1998) Improved social and language skills after secretin administration in patients with autistic spectrum disorders. *Journal of the Association for Academic Minority Physicians* **9** 9–15.

45 See the Repligen Company website for latest information: www.repligen.com

Resources

EarlyBird: A pilot project set up in South Yorkshire by:

The National Autistic Society
393 City Road
London EC1V 1NG
Telephone: 020 7833 2299
Fax: 020 7833 9666
Email: nas@nas.org.uk
Web: www.oneworld.org/autism-uk

Irlen Lens Centre
4 Park Farm Business Centre
Fornham St Genevieve
Bury St Edmunds
Suffolk IP28 6TS
Telephone/Fax: 01284 724301
Web: www.mailbase.ac.uk/lists-p-7/senco-forum

PEACH
Parents for the Early Intervention of Autism in Children
(Behavioural interventions based on the work by Dr Ivar Lovaas)

PEACH
Brunel University
School of Education
St Margaret's Road
Twickenham
Middlesex TW1 1PT
Telephone: 020 8891 0121
Email: peach@brunel.ac.uk

TEACCH
SFTAH
199/203 Blandford Avenue
Kettering
Northants NN16 9AT
Telephone: 01536 523274